QUACK ATTACK

QUACK ATTACK

A Medical Odyssey

Brian Kinney

Matador
9 Priory Business Park,
Wistow Road, Kibworth Beauchamp,
Leicestershire. LE8 0RX
Tel: 0116 279 2299
Email: books@troubador.co.uk
Web: www.troubador.co.uk/matador
Twitter: @matadorbooks

ISBN 978 1 8004 6515 2

British Library Cataloguing in Publication Data.
A catalogue record for this book is available from the British Library.

Printed and bound in Great Britain by 4edge Limited
Typeset in 11pt Garamond Pro by Troubador Publishing Ltd,
Leicester, UK

Matador is an imprint of Troubador Publishing Ltd

This book is dedicated to Pat, who in sickness and in health made me a better man than I otherwise would have been.

PREFACE

The definition of insanity is doing the same over and over expecting a different result.

I was wondering when I was going to write this book. I thought about it many times, but our journey was incomplete. After years of struggling, the unanswered questions seemed to never end. I have spent thousands of hours doing hard research, soul searching, going against all accepted norms, getting angry and disheartened, as well as shouldering the loss of family and friends. After going through jargon-filled medical journals and test results, I chanced upon, of all things, a medical documentary on Netflix called *The Bleeding Edge*. This new information best fit the time frame of the creeping neurological symptoms that Pat had developed over the years. Netflix enlightened where Google searches and trained professionals could not...who would have thought? This wasn't the first time I would stumble upon a piece of the puzzle; sometimes luck is your strongest ally. It answered a question I had asked years ago that was ignored by the medical professionals. I know now, if many of my unanswered questions had been looked into, Pat may have made a full recovery or, at least, she may have not gotten as ill. After years of inexplicable behavioural changes that finally came crashing down upon us, I have all the "best fit" answers I need to tell our story.

This book chronicles my journey as a medical advocate for Pat.

It is not easy to remain an impartial advocate for someone who is near and dear to you. My endocrine system completely took over on several occasions and emotions can override reason, no matter how much of a game face you put on. Many times I was confronted with doubts and my determination was seriously challenged. Somehow a strength and resolve would always rise to the surface from a reservoir that I didn't know I had. I attributed this to my Christian faith. My Irish temper isn't pretty, but was useful on occasion. I was accused of denial by health care professionals and family alike. It seemed I was butting heads with everyone because what they were saying just didn't make any sense. The non-science from a science-and-evidence-based medical system sounded more and more like nonsense to me. This kept nagging me in the back of my mind. I wanted an accurate diagnosis, not speculation. This is one of the most important lessons I learned on this journey: never place blind faith in a medical system.

I was raised in a family that only went to a doctor when a bone was broken or stitches were needed. I assumed, like most people, that medicine was a scientific and evidence-based system. That assumption quickly changed after Pat got sick. Everything changes when it becomes personal. Surprisingly, much of the medical care Pat was receiving was guessing and shots in the dark at best. To assess the care that was being given to Pat, I relied heavily on common sense (the least used knowledge in the world), but I also had basic knowledge of biology and chemistry from the first-year college courses I took. Many times, what was being presented as medicine and science didn't even pass the scrutiny of these rudimentary courses. I have a degree in instructional design for computer-assisted training materials. Designing computer-based training products so that students can learn independently on their own needs to be structured very carefully. This training gave me critical thinking skills that also helped in assessing Pat's medical care. In addition to the knowledge base I had accumulated, I had direct hands-on experience inside the medical system from managing Pat's medical practice. I never intended to get involved in Pat's practice, nor did I want to, but she kept complaining that the business side of her practice was out of control. Medical schools do not train doctors in the business side of running a private practice. I started with finance, and over time I got involved in virtually every other aspect of managing a medical office. I was filling out forms for blood tests, faxing off referrals to specialists, and getting to know the medical services that were offered. The combination of having been raised in a family that rarely went to a doctor and an inside look at how the medical system worked provided me with a unique perspective as a medical advocate.

We spent five long, arduous years in mainstream medicine that only resulted in further decline in Pat's health. This led us into exploring what some of the alternative/complementary medical approaches had to offer. It was a big step for Pat to consider medical approaches outside of mainstream medicine, where she had spent her entire career. The alternative medicine world encompasses a wide spectrum of approaches, with some of it being very exotic, and careful discernment is necessary. She overcame her reluctance after several hours of research revealed that many medical approaches considered alternative in Canada were actually a part of mainstream medical systems in several European countries, Japan and Israel. The inclusion of complementary approaches in their systems not only added credibility in her mind but also narrowed the field of possibilities that may be of benefit to her. It is not easy to look beyond the paradigms and biases inherit in medical approaches to determine its merits, but it was necessary for her to temporarily suspend what she knew about medicine and adopt an open mind. However, the exercise was worth it because it revealed approaches that did produce actual results in the end.

Another important source of information were online patient groups. Anecdotal experiences are dismissed by too many patients and doctors and are in fact a necessary part of medicine. As much as medicine strives to be scientific and evidence-based, patients do not have uniform body chemistry or personalities and thorough medical care needs to take this into account. There are just too many variables to confine any given treatment or therapy to a single reproducible outcome from patient to patient, so patient feedback to judge its effectiveness is essential. I've had discussions with medical researchers and they believe the remedy for the shortcomings of a scientific/evidence medical system is more evidence and more science. None of the researchers I spoke to had any clinical experience and that would explain their myopic view and dismissal of patient experiences. The fact that too many researchers disregard the "anecdotal" patient experience is evidence that there is a disconnect between the medical science community and the front line doctors who treat patients. Ideally, there would be a bilateral flow of information between these two groups that would lead to the refinement and effectiveness of health care. Unfortunately, this not what has developed in the current model of the health care system. Information only flows one way, from the research community to the physician. As such, the disregard of the patient experience has filtered down to the clinical level by what I term as algorithmic medicine. Patient profiling and standards of care are replacing the physician's experience in treating patients and the intuitive sense that develops over years of practice. Ignoring anecdotal information provided from patients is tantamount to ignoring the patient and I would experience this many times throughout our journey.

Another driver for this trend comes from the medical industry. Characterizing the medical system as the medical/industrial complex is not an overstatement. In 1955, when Dr. Jonas Salk was asked who owned the patent on the polio vaccine he developed, his response was, "the people own the patent". The funding for his research and development came from small donations. Now medical research gets a lot of its funding from the medical industry with its large pool of cash. Just be clear, I am not against free enterprise. The private sector has provided mankind with innovations that have benefited all of us.

Free enterprise achieves success by providing products or services that the market is willing to pay for and never loses sight of the end user it serves. The joining at the hip of the medical system with industry has effectively excluded the end user out of its feedback loop. The only industries that I know of that do not have to consider their customers are monopolies. Monopolized industries inevitably come to depend upon cronyism for their existence and quality assurance will decline when this business model doesn't depend on performance.

It was not uncommon for us to find other physicians in the online patient groups who were also looking for answers to their unresolved health issues. Some had become so disillusioned with the medical/industrial complex that they walked away. Their reasons for leaving were enlightening and also validated our decision to look outside mainstream medicine for answers. Also present in the groups were former medical industrial people who shared their experiences in the industry and their reasons for leaving. In the end, I could no longer deny the red pill realization that had been knocking at my awareness for some time now. Despite our connections with some of the best doctors in their field, they delivered nothing. Having exhausted what mainstream medicine had to offer, we felt we had no choice but to walk away. It is not my intention to promote one medical approach over another; we were only interested in results, regardless of where they came from.

Conspiracies? sometimes...agendas, always. We found that nothing can be taken for granted. The choice of treatments, drugs and therapies are influenced by business interests, but also the political philosophy and agendas of a medical system's administration. For whatever reason there is a significant amount of mainstream medicine based on very little science. Some alternative medicine had sound scientific reasoning behind them others were outright fraudulent quackery. So what do you do when trying to get the best medical care for you or your loved one? You need to understand that a higher education does not replace common sense – if you do not have a science or medical background, you can start with that. Ask questions from your medical providers. A skilled medical provider can bypass confusing scientific/medical jargon and use common language to explain what is being done. A good health care provider also has the necessary patience to communicate to their patients. These are two important qualities that you need to watch for in deciding who to choose as your provider. I hope our experiences will inspire and give hope for those who are dealing with an illness or a family member who is ill. The biggest takeaway I hope you get from this book is the importance of getting involved in your own health care. In my opinion, this is absolutely necessary; not to sound melodramatic, but your life may depend on it. There is a lot of lip service about getting involved in your own health, some sincere, some just patronizing. There is a lot of bad medicine out there and you need to do your own due diligence. You do not need a medical degree. Common sense, attentive listening and you can't be timid to ask questions; it is your health, or that of a loved one, at stake.

This is our story; this is what happened to us.

CHANCE MEETING

When a love takes your
breath away…
let it.
Let it suspend you in time
just for a moment.
Surrender to it.

I saw a bumper sticker that said, "To a dog, every fifteen minutes is a brand new day". What a great attitude to adopt. Wisdom is all around if you have your eyes open to it. In the spring of 1990, I moved back to the east coast of Canada. I had been living in Vancouver British Columbia for the previous five years. A divorce and the high cost of living removed any reason for me to be there. I was at a crossroads and this was a good time to start a new life. A change in geography can sometimes help with that. I had never been enthusiastic about living in Atlantic Canada, but that's where I grew up and I still had family and friends there. So, along with my son, we set off on the long drive from the west coast to the east coast. We initially stayed with my parents in north-western New Brunswick for a couple of weeks before moving to our final destination in Moncton. Kent county in south-eastern NB was where my mother's family was from. Moncton was one of the larger towns and there would be more opportunity there for my son and me. We had arranged to rent my cousin's beachside cottage until we could find more permanent housing. Living beachside in August was pleasant, but, as fall turned into winter, the winds from the Northumberland Strait were getting chilly and that's when we moved into town. The following spring my daughter came for a visit and she decided to stay with her brother and me.

I tried to have a social life by rebuilding relationships with my family and friends, but all of us had built our own lives over the years and we just couldn't pick up where we'd left off in our teenage days. I was a ship with no rudder and life was getting lonely. I had gotten married young and really was clumsy at finding myself single again. The deals I kept making with myself to strengthen my resolve were failing me as well. I was never one to go out doing the club scene, but a local bar had live jazz from 6 to 9 pm every Friday night and I went regularly. One evening a table of four women were sitting directly in my line of sight of the band stand. A dark-haired woman caught my attention right away; I thought she was gorgeous. I may have been clumsy and shy, but one of the women at the table wasn't she motioned for me to come over and I took the opportunity to position myself between her and the dark-haired beauty. I chatted with the woman who invited me, but it was not long before I turned my attention to the woman who originally caught my eye. Her name was Patricia. She had two girls from a previous marriage and had been a single mom for about a year. She was a family doctor. I thought that was interesting. I was raised in a blue-collar home and my social circles were blue collar as well. The small talk was pleasant and when the music ended Patricia, one of her friends and I went across the street to a coffee shop. Most of the conversation was between the two women, which made me feel like a third wheel (my awkwardness kicking in again), so I bid them a good evening and went on my way.

I kept going back every Friday evening hoping that I would see her there. I even found her office number in the Yellow Pages.

I dialled the number, and just got the answering machine. I didn't try to call back because I thought she may not appreciate me calling her office. Several weeks went by and I thought maybe it was just a chance meeting that had come and gone. I decided to move on, but then, one Friday evening at the jazz bar, there she was sitting at a table with her friends again. However, this time I was with someone. She wasn't a love interest, but I wasn't just going to abandon who I came with. *Can you believe this? Damn!* We were in the outer room and had to walk right by past her table to go to listen to the band. As I went by Pat's table, she flashed me a big smile and said hello. Several thoughts rushed through my mind at the same time...*Maybe she is interested after all...But I'm here with someone else...Man, I hope this opportunity presents itself again when I'm alone...*I said hello back and went on to find a table. We couldn't find a table so we went back to the outer room and sat at the bar. I glanced over toward her often, and every time she was looking my way and giving me smiles. *Can you believe this?* I kept saying to myself. The opportunity to meet again didn't take long; I was chatting with the lady I had come with when I felt a tap on my shoulder. I turned and there was Pat, leaning over with her hair draping over one shoulder. With a big smile, she gave me a slip of paper with her phone number and asked me to give her a call. She took me by surprise; at least one of us wasn't shy and clumsy. From that point on, the lady I was with sounded like the adult voices in the Charlie Brown cartoons. I have no recollection of our conversation beyond that point.

I waited a few days before giving her a call, not wanting to appear too anxious. She picked up the phone and said hello. I had no more than got a hello out myself when she asked if I could call back some other time. Short and sweet. I was to find out later she was in the middle of a mini crisis with her two kids. Her daughters had a healthy rivalry and she was settling one of their disputes. It took about a week, but we got together and went out for dinner. We hit it off and started seeing each other. She had been separated from her husband for about a year, which wasn't very long, and I was her first date since she and her husband parted ways. *Hmm…was this going to be a rebound relationship for her?* Rebounds are said not to last. We were both divorced so it was best just to let things evolve organically and see where it goes. It sure felt right, and I knew she was feeling the same; I guess it's true: when you know you know.

We were really hitting it off. We enjoyed each other's company regardless of what we were doing; we went out for dinners; she liked the outdoors so we took a lot of walks; she was health conscious about exercise and she got me into jogging and biking. The more we got to know each other, the more we liked each other. Most importantly, we both liked to laugh; she would almost look for reasons to laugh. She had a witty sense of humour that responded to the moment. I had the corn ball sense of humour that I inherited from my dad – he used to like to clown around a lot. We got pretty good at knowing how to tease each other. She told me she had scored 147 on an IQ test one time and once in a while I would tell her I wasn't seeing that 147 at the moment. She would roll her eyes and said she was sorry she ever told me that. She wasn't bragging when she told me her IQ score; she said EQ (emotional quotient) was more important than IQ anyway, and she was right. The world has a lot of people with "brains" that could be hired for minimum wage: intelligent, but no common sense. She looked at me once and said that I was a lot smarter than I looked. Hmm…compliment given, compliment taken away. Eventually we had disagreements. In the heat of an argument, I told her, "Don't tell me what to do." She just looked at me coyly and said, "I'm not trying to tell you what to do; I'm just trying to instruct you." *WHAT?* That just pissed me off even more. I don't know how the score board would have tallied up, but I think we were about even with the teasing digs.

Pat's doctor lifestyle and being a single parent created problems from time to time. Life's details simply got lost with such a busy schedule. We were driving into town one day and the police had a roadside check set up. I was behind the wheel. As I pulled up and stopped for my turn, the police officer noticed right away that the vehicle's inspection sticker had expired. Strike one. He asked for the insurance and registration. Pat got them out of the glove compartment and I passed it to him. He looked at the documents and said that both the insurance and registration had expired: strike two and three. I am sitting there thinking this is going to cost big time. He asked us to wait a minute and went back to the police car. He came back and looked over at Pat and asked, aren't you my doctor? Pat was one of the doctors for the Royal Canadian Mounted Police. She also was one of the doctors that did air crew medicals for pilots and air traffic controllers also. Pat responded, "Yes, I am your doctor." He gave us a stern look and gave us ten days to bring up the vehicle's paperwork to date. I said, "Yes sir, we'll do this expeditiously". Thank God for some of the small perks of being a doc in the community. While we were driving off she said, "I have no idea who that cop was." Oh well, we still dodged a bullet.

A physician's office is not without its adventures either. We had an elderly couple come in and the lady was feeling really sick with the flu. She went into the bathroom and we heard her fall. Oh no, this could be trouble. Pat went in and she had fallen forward while sitting on the toilet and went head first into the wall. Her head made a hole in the sheet rock the size of her skull. Her husband was standing in the bathroom doorway and said to her, "Well, dear, at least you missed the stud." Pat would set aside some days to do nothing but female pelvic exams. The pap smears were put in the small refrigerator we had in the office and she would take them all to the lab at the hospital at the end of day. We had a beautiful blue-eyed husky dog, but he was as dumb as a fence post. She had him in the car one time when she was making a run to the lab and had to stop to gas up. While she went into the service station to pay for the gas, Blue, our husky, thought that the pap smears were a dog treat and he mangled them. Pat made some excuse and got the women back in again to do the exam over. I guess you could call

5

this a bizarre variation on the dog ate my homework.

It's considered not good medicine for doctors to treat friends and family. Pat was really stringent in following that rule. Problem was, I had just as much trouble accessing my primary care physician like everybody else. I kept bugging her to do simple things for me like a throat swab instead of having to wait days or weeks to see my PCP. I thought I should get an extra perk by her helping me out once in a while. I didn't need much; I rarely went to a doctor. No such luck: she wouldn't budge. After years of nagging her, she finally gave in. I needed her to do a throat swab for me and drop it off to the lab. The results would go to my doctor and he would take it from there. Simple. She asked me to go to one of the examining rooms and jump up onto the examining to do the swab. She said open your mouth and say ahh…I had no more than gotten my mouth open when she stuck that swab stick in my mouth and rattled it around in the back of my throat like she was using a bottle washer. In and out in the blink of an eye. Wow! I asked her why in Hell she did that. She said she always does it that way to bypass any gag reflex. That was the last time I ever asked her to do anything for me.

Doctors are trained in medicine and receive no training in operating the business side of private medical practice. Doctors don't even think of their practices in these terms. Like any business it has expenses, rent to be paid, supplies, payroll to be met, etc. Pat had a hard time to balance a checkbook let alone assuming those responsibilities. She was always complaining to me about being behind on her bills. Most importantly, she was severely behind on making her quarterly income tax instalments. She kept asking me to help her out, but I didn't have any experience in running a business either. Besides, I had completed my degree in multi media design and was interested in pursuing a new career. Despite my reservations and having no business experience, I started looking into business operation of her practice. It soon became obvious that the business finances were out of control. Canada has a single payer medical system that paid bi-weekly and reluctantly I started going in every two weeks and just started by making sure the bills were paid and were not falling behind. The largest expenditure was the quarterly income tax remissions and she had fallen seriously behind on the instalments. Compounding the problem was penalties were being added on to the quarterly remissions making the problem even more difficult to tame. It took some time to bring this under control.

The Canadian single payer government-run medical system creates a unique situation for doctors who are in private practice. If a business incurs an increase in operating costs, they have the option of increasing their prices and passing that on to the customer. The pay scale for physicians is negotiated by the medical society and the provincial governments and, if costs go up, the practice has to absorb it. My involvement started in the background doing budgeting and gradually over time I assumed more responsibilities right down to the custodial work. I would do anything to reduce expenses. She did some extra billing services outside of Medicare and that was also totally disorganized. She had no idea who had paid and who didn't. She also wasn't maximizing her extra billing opportunities and was doing things for no remuneration. I gradually took on more of the office duties. I started taking care of paperwork, sending off blood requisitions, sending referrals to specialists and near the end of her practice I replaced her secretary and worked the front of the office, manning the phone and booking patients. I took a lot of flack for this from people thinking of me as nothing more than a doctor's wife. Pat said the job came with the perk that I got to fuck the boss. Now what in Hell was I supposed to say to something like that? I didn't have a snappy comeback for that one, so she got one up on the scoreboard in the teasing battle.

Our long-term plans after the kids all had graduated from high school was to move to a warmer climate in the US. I was raised in a border community and my father worked on the US side. I had a lot of family extending down into New England on both sides of my family. Pat had spent her high school years in Washington, DC, so both of us felt comfortable stateside. Pat's father was a Canadian federal civil servant and his last posting was in the DC area. They bought a home just across the Potomac River in Arlington, Virginia. The house included an in-law suite in the basement with its own entrance and Pat lived a semi-autonomous life style in it. This move was in the middle of the politically and culturally charged times of the late Sixties. Pat had even had a boyfriend who worked on Bobby Kennedy's campaign. He was drafted and sent to Vietnam after high school, so the issues of the time were very real to Pat as it was for many others. The late teens are very formative years that shapes our views well into adulthood and that particular era made a big impression on everyone.

Back on the home front, I worked in construction as a carpenter for years and I took off the office manager hat and put on the carpenter's hat to renovate the house. Pat bought the house before we met and I wish I could have been there before she bought it. She liked it because of its contemporary design, but it needed a lot of work. The house had been built in the Seventies and it had all this ugly stucco texture stuff on the ceilings. The living room had nineteen-foot vaulted ceilings. I gutted the room to get rid of all the ugly stucco, which was on the upper half of the walls too. The house was cold so I took the opportunity to upgrade the insulation, seal up anything that could cause a draft and installed a proper vapour barrier. Along with the new windows, the insulation upgrade really warmed up the house. I rented a wheel-around scaffold to work on the ceiling. I have to admit that I curse a lot when I get frustrated and Pat hated it. She would disappear into the bedroom to avoid listening my bitching. She would only come out if she didn't hear me sounding off just to make sure I hadn't fallen off the scaffold and was lying on the floor unconscious. We put in new flooring, a steel roof and a beautiful new front door. The choice for the new front door was one of the rare occasions when we agreed on something and no discussion needed. By the time we were done, the house looked great. All told, we lived in that house for twenty-one years before we eventually sold it and moved away.

All these anecdotal snapshots of our backgrounds and the life we had together is to give the reader an understanding of how the troubles that were to come along and the significant health issues that were to emerge in 2006 completely changed the trajectory of our lives.

FROM MED SCHOOL
TO MED PRACTICE

Life is what happens to you while you're busy making other plans
John Lennon (line from the song "Beautiful Boy")

A critical event happened to Pat at a very early age: her mother was diagnosed with breast cancer when Pat was only a toddler. This left Pat with a deep scar and a fear of death that followed her the rest of her life. This traumatic experience was particularly driven home because Pat was hospitalized for an infection at the same time her mother was hospitalized for cancer. Despite each of their wards being close by, neither of them could come to visit the other. This deep-seated fear would be the elephant in the room that would come to haunt us many times over the next few years in our journey to resolve Pat's health issues. When Pat was in her late twenties, her mother developed breast cancer again and this time she wouldn't survive. Pat had followed in her father's footsteps and got a job with the federal civil service, but she didn't like working as a civil servant and left the position to move back to Atlantic Canada so she could help her father take care of her ailing mother. They took care of her at home until she passed away.

Now that her mother was gone and she didn't have a job, she decided to go to medical school. She mentioned to me once that she decided to go to medical school to help her understand her mother's death, so, in a way, it was a part of her grieving process in losing her mother. It may have been a coping mechanism, but I think it was just a part of her ways. I would watch her more than once over the next few years research her own health issues to the point where she knew as much or more than the specialists treating her. She applied to Dalhousie medical school, but was at a disadvantage because she only had an arts degree with a French major. The head of the medical faculty sympathized because, when he decided to go into medicine, he only had an arts degree as well. He told her, if she could get the required science credits during the summer sessions, he would consider her to be accepted to the medical program. There was a reason that Pat was never that good at sciences: she hated it. She got through calculus, chemistry, physics and biology in the two months of July and August. Summer courses may not be as extensive as the regular classes, but there is still a lot of compressed information to digest to achieve the credit. I was impressed when she told me that. I needed a tutor to help me get through some of those first-year sciences, but Pat did it on sheer determination. She passed the courses with acceptable grades and was accepted to Dalhousie medical school. The academic environment suited Pat's personality. She wasn't a party girl and never did drugs or drink alcohol. She didn't like being impaired and I never saw her have more than two glasses of wine at social events. She would jokingly touch the end of her nose and, if it felt a little numb, that was the end of that evening's alcohol intake.

The Canadian Armed Forces recruited Pat while she was in medical school. After graduation she served for a few years and they in turn paid for her education. Since she was a physician she was entering service with the rank of captain, but she still had to go through boot camp. To be sure, this was a baby boot camp compared to what enlisted men experienced, but she was four months pregnant when she did it. The most memorable story she told me from that time was when she had to rappel down a forty-foot wall. Pat is deathly afraid of heights and I would have liked to been there to witness that one. She was all harnessed up and she was hanging over the edge of the wall with just her tip toes on the edge. It was at this point that she looked directly in the eyes of the drill instructor and yelled "FUCK YOU!" An enlisted recruit would have been in deep trouble if they had done that, but in her case they overlooked this infraction because she was going to be serving as a doctor and the military needed them. She was required to experience some of the different branches of the military. She spent some time on a frigate out on the North Atlantic, but her most memorable experience was as a passenger in a fighter jet. The pilot did a barrel roll for her. I used to tease her because she was afraid to take rides with me on my Harley-Davidson even with assurances that I wouldn't barrel roll the bike. She had seen too many motorcycle injuries come through the emergency room and wasn't willing to take the risk.

After her military service, she decided move back to her hometown to be closer to her father. She opened up her own private medical practice and was ready to settle down and raise her young family. Pat was interested in all aspects of medicine. In addition to her practice, she did emergency room shifts, which she called macho medicine. She did surgical assists and was one of the few GPs in the community that did obstetrics. Obstetrics was her favourite part of the job; she called that happy medicine. In time, the babies she delivered grew into young women and started having babies of their own and she delivered them too. Many doctors like to supplement their incomes outside of the single-payer Canadian medical monopoly. Since remuneration from the government system was fixed, an income source outside the system would help off set the rising costs of doing business. An older doctor who did air crew medicals for pilots and air traffic control personnel was retiring and offered the opportunity to Pat. She also did medicals for members of the Royal Canadian Mounted Police. Another opportunity arose from another retiring doctor who was the base surgeon at the local Canadian Forces Base. Since Pat had served in the military, he suggested that she apply for the position; she did and was accepted. It was four hours a week doing sick parade and taking care of military personnel's needs going to and coming back from Afghanistan. There was an alarming growth of the population who could not find a primary care physician. To mitigate the problem, the government allowed "after hours clinics" to open up. Pat became part owner of one these clinics. She did shifts in the clinic as well as several other clinics in the area.

Pat started developing hip pain 2005. She delayed having an assessment, hoping that it would get better, but instead it just progressively got worse. Pat's determination sometimes manifests as a stupid stubbornness. She finally went to see an orthopaedic surgeon and he diagnosed her hip with osteoarthritis. The surgeon said that a hip replacement would be inevitable at some point. She procrastinated over having the surgery and was worried about the loss of income. I was taught some physiotherapy, which we did in the evenings after coming home from the office. The physio wasn't providing any relief and in 2006 she decided to go through with hip replacement surgery. We didn't realize at the time, but this decision would prove to be catastrophic to her health over the next few years. The common practice for doctors who were going to be away from their office was to hire a locum to continue seeing patients. Locums are physicians who operate as free-floating agents who may not want to have a practice of their own or maybe young recently graduated doctors who haven't set up their own practice yet. The usual arrangement is for the locum to keep one third of the billings and the other two thirds pays for the office expenses. This is a huge benefit because now all you need is money to cover your personal expenses while you are off work. It can be difficult to find a locum to take your place, but we did and the hip surgery was scheduled for April 3, 2006.

Pat was only fifty-six years old when she needed the hip replacement. This is quite young. She also had other joint issues, some arthritis in her hands and bunions on her feet. She had one of the bunions corrected and also had a hammer toe that was corrected with surgery. It was nine years later that a naturopath would ask the obvious question: why is she having so many joint issues at a young age? Good question. The orthopaedic surgeon made the offhand suggestion that her hip damage may have resulted from a sports injury that happened years ago. The only sport that Pat participated in when she was young was swimming. She wasn't into team sports she was too much of a loner for that and swimming was too low impact to have caused hip degeneration. It was always in the back of my mind that her hip damage wasn't from a sports-related injury. I didn't get beyond my intuitive sense because we all accept what doctors tell you…right? Questioning and doubting is an attitude that I regret that I hadn't developed earlier. Hindsight is always 20/20, but, if I'd done so, Pat's health issues could have been avoided or at least not as severe. I think all of us want answers to a problem if one is to be found. Investigating underlying conditions and identifying factors that could lead to problems before they occur is a much better quality of medical care. The medical community indeed does investigations, but, rather than being patient specific, investigations are guided by very generic statistics gathered from the general population. The surgery had the desired effect: her hip pain was gone. She was even able to resume her physical activities like jogging and exercise classes. We thought the problem was solved, but years later the hip prosthetic would be a major source of the health problems that were to develop later on.

In 2007 during a routine annual physical exam, Pat was dealt a second serious blow. Her primary care physician noticed that Pat's liver had an abnormal shape. Her PCP sent a referral to a gastroenterologist for further investigations. He ordered a blood test and found her iron levels were 2647.1 µg/L (should be around 100 µg/L) and iron saturation virtually at 100 percent! He had never seen or even heard of levels this high before. Her gastroenterologist wanted to put her on disability on the spot. He suspected that she may have haemochromatosis and ordered a genetic test to confirm it. She tested positive for the two genetic mutations that lead to hemochromatosis. Fatigue is one of the symptoms for hemochromatosis and maybe this was the explanation for Pat's growing fatigue over the previous few years. She also had other telltale signs of the disease, hair loss and the "bronzing" skin discoloration of her feet and ankles. Progressive symptoms can easily be missed as a sign of a brewing medical problem. Pat thought her increasing fatigue was just because she was aging. I noticed it too and I was concerned that it might be burn out instead. She had been cutting back on medicine over the last few years. The first to go were the emergency room shifts, but she eventually had to give up doing obstetrics as well. This was a disappointing decision for her because she loved delivering babies. It was I who convinced her to give up obstetrics. It was getting difficult for her to do deliveries in the middle of the night and then see patients at the office the next day. It came to head when one week she did deliveries in the middle of the night on three consecutive days followed with a full office. She was exhausted.

Medicine had changed over the course of Pat's career. There were more therapies, more drugs available, more investigations that could be ordered and doctor's autonomy was being eroded by standards of care and patient profiling. It wasn't clear to me that this was increasing the quality of medicine, but it was certainly increasing the cost of health care. The patients in Pat's practice were also getting older, requiring more time. Pat had her closed her practice to new patients years ago, but it was still expanding because children she had cared for were now grown up having children of their own and Pat took them into her practice. Patients were getting frustrated because she had cut back on office hours due to her own fatigue. These factors and the toxic work environment at the hospital were really starting to take a toll early in 2008. All of this at a time when she was getting more and more tired.

In 1980 the doctor/patient ratio for the community was about one physician for every 5000 patients. Patients were still able to go from doctor to doctor settling on one they preferred. By 2008, the ratio was about one physician for every 410 patients. Despite this improved patient/doctor ratio, approximately twenty percent of the community did not have access to a primary care doctor. So how did this happen? Publicly the government said they were trying to solve the problem, but this didn't explain why a surgeon and a hematologist who had moved to the area were just provided general practitioner licences. These two doctors took some of Pat's patients when she eventually closed her practice. They had immigrated from Africa and were really nice guys. The surgeon was able to assist in surgeries, offering his expertise for a drastically reduced pay scale. At that time the hospital had one operating room that only functioned for a half-hour a week because of lack of staff. Not allowing this doctor to apply his full surgical skills was a serious disservice to the community. It was the same for the hematologist. Cancer patients in the community were being denied his much-needed specialty. The mismanagement of health care by the provincial government was placing a tremendous strain on physicians as well as the patients. When Pat first started her practice in the Eighties, the relationship within the physician community was cooperative and informal. By the end of her practice, this level of cooperation was replaced by frayed nerves and short tempers. When she first started working at the hospital, administration occupied one half of one floor. When she left a whole new three-floor wing was being built just for administration. Politically driven agendas from a growing administration were creating a very toxic work environment.

Now that Pat was definitively diagnosed with hemochromatosis, two things needed to be done. Imaging of her liver and a biopsy was ordered to see if it could be determined why it was so mishapen. She also had to draw blood (phlebotomies) to get her ferritin count down from 2647.1 µg/L to 50.0 µg/L. Ferritin is a protein that stores iron in body tissues and is a more accurate measure for iron overload, whereas testing iron directly only measures iron present in the blood. This required a lot of phlebotomies. She started with a couple a week and was gradually decreased as the feritin was brought down. She would take a couple of glasses of juice prior to the phlebotomy to avoid dehydration from the blood loss, but it also made her very tired. It took months to reach the desired benchmark and her arm looked like a pin cushion by the end of it. Once the levels were stabilized, she had a blood test every three months to check for ferritin levels followed by a phlebotomy if necessary. During this period, Pat was still in full practice and would go to the office an hour or so after her phlebotomy.

Livers are shaped like a wedge. The large lobe of Pat's liver had shrivelled up considerably and the small lobe was enlarged. Livers are remarkably adaptive when they have been damaged. The small lobe had grown larger to compensate for the damaged larger lobe. Pat's daily routine included doing rounds at the hospital for her inpatients. It was on one of her hospital rounds that she met her gastroenterologist in the hallway. She asked him if the results of her liver biopsy had come back. He said it was an inadequate sample, turned and walked away, leaving Pat standing there. She was taken aback and didn't know what to think. Her gastroenterologist had also been a colleague of hers for years. She had referred many of her own patients to this doctor. Pat waited for several weeks and didn't receive an appointment for another biopsy, nor was she contacted by her PCP. Now what?

The liver imaging indicated the possible presence of ascites. Ascites is a fluid and a marker that her liver may have become cancerous. We had no idea how damaged Pat's liver was and she was really worried. Pat decided to be proactive and she contacted her cousin in Massachusetts. Both her cousin and her husband were radiologists. They were sympathetic to Pat's concerns and her husband made arrangements to have a biopsy done at the hospital where he worked. He hand picked the interventional radiologist for the biopsy, the pathologist to interpret the results and even hand picked his preferred imaging technicians to operate the equipment. All the doctors involved waived their professional fees to help a sick colleague. The pathologist was a consultant for a lot of high-profile court cases, but still asked another pathologist to review her findings just to make sure. What a difference in attitude from Pat's own colleagues back home. The US medical system is a tangled web of insurance companies. Some companies pay more for the same procedure and it's all very confusing. Pat's cousin did everything she could to reduce costs for us. We had to pay up front for the biopsy before it could be performed. Pat's cousin came with us to administration to make the payment. Since insurance companies are billed directly, the lady at administration had no idea what to charge. Pat's cousin had negotiated a price beforehand for $750.00 and the lady took her word for it. We gave her our credit card and the biopsy was done. We were here on a serious matter of getting a liver biopsy, but I couldn't help but be amused with this whole exchange.

The biopsy revealed that Pat's liver had cirrhotic tissue. This is not good news because cirrhosis can become cancerous. The good news was that she didn't have ascites. What was thought to be ascites back home was actually her gall bladder. Pat's liver was so deformed that it had squeezed her gall bladder almost flat and this was mistaken for ascites. I couldn't help but wonder how this misinterpretation could occur. Did they not notice the gall bladder wasn't visible? I'm not a radiologist, but wouldn't it be standard to make sure that everything is where it's supposed to be when interpreting images? This was when I first started questioning the level of care her doctors were providing her back home. While Pat was resting after the procedure, her cousin asked if she would like to have a CT of her liver. She had a mischievous smile when she asked. The CT equipment was just across the hall. She pulled back the curtain, looked left and right the hall was empty. Pat was quickly rolled into the CT room and the images were taken. This little cloak and dagger escapade gave us a freebie that the hospital would not be aware of.

We hadn't given a heads-up to her gastroenterologist that we were going to Massachusetts to get the biopsy done. When we returned we gave him copies of the biopsy report and the CT imaging summary.

Also included was a management plan for Pat's liver. He thought the plan was good and saw no reason for him not to implement it. We didn't tell him the management plan was developed by Pat's radiologist cousin and not a gastroenterologist. Interesting. If a radiologist can put together a suitable liver management plan, then is a gastroenterologist necessary? Plus he still offered no explanation as to why he hadn't ordered a second liver biopsy for Pat after the first failed attempt. We had to travel to another country to get a proper biopsy and properly interpreted liver images from doctors who were complete strangers, all of whom waived their professional fees to help out a sick doctor. This was a direct contrast to the lack of courtesy, the incompetent biopsy, the misinterpretation of liver imaging that she received from her own colleagues that she had worked with for the previous twenty years. This is when I first started questioning the quality of health care that we could expect going forward. My concerns would be justified because the quality of her health care was soon to get exponentially worse. To add insult to injury, the Canadian universal health care system that we paid taxes for all our lives wouldn't cover the costs for the biopsy that was done stateside.

When Pat was diagnosed with hemochromatosis, she started researching the disease in earnest. This was always the coping mechanism that kicked in when she was worried about something. She found one of the leading researchers for hemochromatosis in the world was living in London, Ontario. He didn't do clinical work, but agreed to see her if she got a referral from her current doctor. Pat made an appointment to see her gastroenterologist to get the referral. I went with her to the appointment and while we were there she also brought up the topic of a liver transplant. She just wanted to prepare for any eventuality. He got up off his chair walked around his desk to where we were sitting and started scolding Pat for bringing up liver transplants and for wanting a referral to see the researcher. This caught me off guard. What the hell was going on here? I can concede that discussing a liver transplant may have been an overreaction, but why was he getting so angry? Pat and her father took care of her mother at home with cancer until the day she died and also from her own medical practice saw how ugly a cancer death can be. I came to find out that the hemochromatosis specialist in Ontario was one of his heroes and he knew him personally. So was sending a referral going to cause him personal embarrassment? I don't know nor do I care. We already had to take matters into our own hands after his failed liver biopsy attempt and travel to the US the get the job done right. I made up my mind that he was incompetent and weak if his ego was offended by asking for a referral to see the researcher. That was the last appointment we had with him.

Once again we called upon Pat's cousin in Boston to help us out. We explained what happened and he called a radiologist that he went to medical school with for a recommendation. He suggested contacting a liver transplant surgeon in Halifax and he would call him on Pat's behalf to explain the situation if Pat wanted. The surgeon was originally from Lebanon and had the same attitude as the US doctors and wanted to help out a sick colleague. He broke protocol and allowed Pat to jump the patient queue for an early appointment. The surgeon and his triage nurse were courteous and attentive at the appointment. He agreed to be the point man in managing Pat's liver from now on. Pat would have an annual appointment with him mostly to hold her place in the surgical queue just in case her liver went south and she would have to have a liver transplant. The blood tests every three months would continue as before, but, where she was getting an MRI for her liver every six months, now it would be alternating ultrasounds and MRIs at the six-month intervals. Her PCP and the gastroenterologist back home were provided the blood test and the imaging results, but were no longer directly involved in managing Pat's liver. Meanwhile, Pat decides to continued her full medical practice.

OK... SO WE
KEEP GOING

Passions can keep you alive

Pat loved medicine. She really enjoyed her patients. She had stopped obstetrics a few years ago, but many of the mothers who she delivered a generation before were starting families of their own and she took the new babies into her practice. She enjoyed her older patients as well. A couple of her elderly patients passed away and had no family to attend the funeral services and Pat was the only one there to pay respects. Pat's practice had been closed for several years, but one day a senior gentleman came to the office and asked her if she would accept him into her practice. He told Pat that he had worked as civil servant in the same office where her father and mother worked. So Pat decided as a courtesy to take him on as a patient. He would tell her stories about those days and how he and Pat's father had been competing for her mother's attention. He chuckled that not only had her father won her attention, he won her hand in marriage. He said when he realized that her father was her mother's choice, he sat back and watched their romance blossom before his eyes. Pat was delighted to hear this third-party perspective on her parents. It stirred her imagination of what her parents were like before she came along. Her parents were of the "greatest generation". The entire trajectory of their lives and their world view were shaped by the ravages of a world war. It was also a time when chivalry played a big part in courtships. Gentlemen opened the car door and held the chair for the ladies to sit down. Pat remembered her father smiling and saying that, in his day, a woman would never consider going out in public without wearing gloves on her hands. Pat's father stood at six feet, five inches tall. I called him the gentle giant because of his mild demeanour. He was quiet and soft spoken. Pat's maternal grandfather died in his fifties. This left Pat's mother, the oldest of her siblings, to assume a more parental role to help her mother raise the family.

A source of strength and a refuge for Pat was the whole family going to her father's house on Thursday evening for dinner. He would spend the day meticulously preparing a meal for us including home-baked pies. After the meal we would just hang out and wait for his favourite game show to come on the television. He faithfully watched his favourite game show every day. Pat's daughters went to school near by and went to granddad's every day for lunch and Pat would pick them up everyday after work there too. Many of their classmates lived in the neighbourhood and grand dad's served as a second home. One night I brought over a video of Riverdance, an Irish dance troupe. There was a segment in the video with some flamenco dancers and it reminded Pat's father of an event during the war. The ship he was serving on had a layover in Gibraltar. They were given some shore leave and he with some of his buddies went to a bar where some flamenco dancers were performing. He said, after a few drinks, "Me and the boys decided to jump up on stage and help them out." He laughed and said that it wasn't long before the shore patrol came along and threw them all in jail. At first Pat laughed and then expressed shock that her father had been in jail. That was completely out of character from the father that she knew. He was a "gentle giant" but was known on rare occasions to unleash a formidable temper. Although Pat was a daddy's girl, a few times she would be on the receiving end of his wrath if she disrespected her mother. That was a line you didn't cross and she got the message loud and clear. Pat's father had been raised by his widowed mother and had a deep respect for women and motherhood.

The College of Physicians and Surgeons, recommended size for a medical practice was 1100 patients. However, Pat and most of her colleagues had approximately 2500 or more. Many younger doctors had practices that were less than the recommended 1100 patients. When she eventually decided to close her practice it took five doctors to take on her patients. A perfect storm was starting to take shape and something had to give. At a time when Pat needed to slow down, the pressure was on for her to do more from several different angles. Pat would typically see on average forty-five patients a day, but by the end of 2008 it was down to about forty-five a week. Trying to schedule appointments to meet patient demand was becoming impossible. With Pat's self preservation on the line, I had no choice but to keep reducing appointments. As the appointments gradually decreased, patient frustrations increased. Confrontations was almost a daily occurrence and I used joke when I unlocked the office door that it was show time. It was getting to be a very stressful situation for both of us and there were many days I left the office with chest pain. Pat had closed the practice from taking new patients years ago with the exception of newborn babies from patients in her practice. She had stop this as well, which was a disappointment for her and the families.

Remuneration for physicians may be unique among professionals. Comparing a medical practice to a law practice, for example, a law office can direct bill everything to their clients right down to a postage stamp. Medical office expenses from the rent down to tongue depressors are paid for by the fee for service and none of it is direct billed to the patient. This means, when expenses go up, it is absorbed by the practice with no way to recoup the rise in operating costs. Another important distinction is lawyers for, example, bill for their time spent on task. Physicians, on the other hand, get paid the same fee for service for each patient regardless of their health issue. Most billings were a code one, which at the time paid $37.66. This was the fee paid for a five-minute appointment to renew a prescription or a two-hour appointment with patients with complicated health issues. So her aging patients requiring more care was creating a double-edged sword effect. The longer appointments were causing income to go down and it also resulted in fewer available appointments, frustrating patients already trying to get an appointment. So the irony is there is no money in treating the sicker patients. Then there were disability insurance claims. The standard that most the insurance companies would pay was fifty dollars. A simple claim update could take hours of chart review. When we tried to bill for the time taken for the report, their response was that any additional costs were the patient's responsibility. In most cases patients simply couldn't afford to pay for the report because they weren't working. So once again this cost was being absorbed by the practice. Additionally, if the reports were not submitted in a timely manner the doctor could be held legally responsible if a delay affected the claim. Pat loved medicine, but the business of medicine was causing more and more stress and draining the enjoyment out of the job.

Pat started taking on more shifts at the after-hours clinics. For the most part, the clinic market was for the renewal of prescriptions, flu shots, taking temps, doctor notes for employers and other light-duty work. Clinics didn't keep patient charts and they didn't do hospital admissions. The clinics booked the patients, did the billing and all a doctor had to do was show up for the shift and when the shift was done, simply walk out the door and go home. Many of Pat's contemporaries were winding down their practices and opting to do more clinic shifts as well. A couple of doctors also had health issues and they needed to slow down as well. The after-hours clinics were not without controversy. The hospital's view was that clinics didn't provide the continuity of care that a patient would receive if they had their own doctor. The high-minded opinion of the hospital that walk-in clinics provided substandard care was questionable particularly since hospitals in other parts of the province didn't have the same concerns about the clinics in their communities. There were some doctors who shared the same opinion as the hospital. They may have been sincere, but what I noticed was none of these doctors worked in the clinic themselves. They were losing their "easy money" appointments for BP checks, flu shots, etc. to the clinics and their incomes were being affected. However, their patients had to wait for weeks for simple prescription refills so they went to the clinics instead. The controversy didn't mean anything to the 25 percent of the community who couldn't find a family doctor. For these people, clinics were the only access they had to the medical system. A case in point was one clinic that positioned itself in a niche market doing well woman exams. There were many women in the community who didn't have a doctor and were not getting regular pelvic and breast exams, so there was a need. Furthermore, to see a specialist a referral is needed from a PCP. Pat was one of the doctors who worked at this well woman clinic and she examined one woman who had an oozing breast lesion and she referred her to the specialist that she needed. Pat was doubtful if this woman was going to survive. This patient was likely going to pay with her life for having not having a doctor of her own. Working this clinic gave Pat a lot of job satisfaction knowing that she was making a significant contribution to women's health in the community. She would come to find out later that this much-needed service didn't mean a thing to hospital administration.

Patients who had a salaried doctor had an exponentially more difficult time getting an appointment with their doctors. The option for doctors to go on salary was the government's attempt to control the increasing costs of health care. The salaried doctors saw a fraction of patients on any given day compared to a fee for service doctor. Salaried doctors had no financial incentive to book a lot of appointments because they received a steady paycheck no matter what. It may have taken weeks for a patient to have an appointment with their fee for service doctors, but getting an appointment with a salaried doctor could take months. Many of the salaried doctors went through an internship program at the hospital and were groomed into the hospital's way of thinking. One of these doctors became the head of family medicine. There is no continuity of care when it can take months to see one of these doctors. This double standard was acceptable to the hospital because these doctors were a part of their system and the after-hours walk-in clinics were not. Putting doctors on salary may have helped the spiralling out-of-control costs of the health system, but the low volume salaried doctors made it even more difficult for the public to gain access to the health care system. This is a good example of when a system takes precedent over the community that it serves. This concerned and frustrated the older doctors because they couldn't depend on the younger salaried doctors to fill the void when they wanted to retire. There was another problem that concerned the veteran doctors. Although seeing forty-five to sixty patients a day may have resulted in not spending enough time with some patients, the higher patient volume did give them a lot more experience than a salaried doc who maybe saw 8-10 patients a day. Salaried doctors were reluctant to treat certain issues like toddlers or babies with heavy vomiting or diarrhea. Those small bodies can't lose fluids as much as a grown up and they can be in danger quickly. Instead of dealing with it, these doctors many times sent those young patients to the emergency room, where they were seen by a pediatrician. Older doctors saw this an abdication of patient care.

On December 24, 2008, the inevitable happened, Pat closed her practice. Even though we had cut way back on office appointments and she did lighter-duty after-hours clinic work, she was still burning the candle at both ends. A few of her call group doctors were also personal friends and they expressed concern for her. They had already closed their practices and were encouraging her to do the same. She was closing the practice, but would continue the after hours clinic shifts, including the well woman clinic. I was relieved. She was particularly glad she wouldn't have to be on call anymore. I think for most doctors taking care of their inpatients was the most stressful part of their job. It was necessary to be a part of a call group or else a doctor would be on call 24/7, 365 days a year. Doctors would form call groups so they could have some time away from medicine and spend some time with their families. If a call group had seven doctors, this meant that each doctor would be on call one day of the week and a one weekend call every seventh weekend. This gave some time off, but it also meant that, when you were on call, you were not only taking care of your inpatients, but the other six doctor's inpatients as well. A doctor knew their patients, but not knowing the patients of the other six doctors could be stressful and complicated depending on why the patient was admitted.

I started noticing subtle changes in Pat's behaviour that I attributed to burn out and I hoped closing the practice would give her the respite that she needed to recharge her batteries. Pat was a voracious reader and would read at least one novel a week. She would even read place mats at restaurants. She had the annoying habit of flinging a book across the bed when she had finished reading it. As if she had vanquished another conquest: "there, I'm done with you". Many times I was in the direct line of fire of that airborne conquest and I eventually got fed up and returned the volley: "there, right back at you". Her junk food reading as she called it, started to slow down to the point where she just holding an open book without reading it. She would stop by her father's house every morning for breakfast before going to the office. She would read the newspaper or some of the several magazine subscriptions her father collected, but that eventually stopped as well. One evening she put a book down and sighed, "Oh, Brian, my brain isn't working right." I wasn't sure what to make of that statement. I asked if she wanted to be seen, but she just brushed it off. Doctors do not make good patients. After a while the reading stopped entirely. She was also faithful to exercise. She had been an avid swimmer from an early age and in the winter she went to the aquatic centre at the high school. She also took exercise classes or went to a gym on a regular basis. When summer arrived she took it outside with jogging, biking and hiking. These activities slowed down and came to a stop as well.

Pat had always been quiet and shy in social situations. She was told more than once growing up that she was eccentric, which contributed to her lack of confidence socially. Where nine out of ten people would approach a problem similarly, Pat was that one out of ten that would find a different path for the solution. Her "eccentricity" was part of her charm to me. She was fully aware of her lack of social graces. So for her to say one day, "I'm acting awkward", really stood out. She was noticing something different about herself. Gradual changes are difficult to identify as a symptom to a growing health problem. I thought the lack of interest in activities she once enjoyed could have been explained away as fatigue. Gradual changes can also incrementally be accepted as a new normal without even realizing it. A case in point, I mentioned to Pat that I had a ringing sound in my ears. She told me that I had a neurological disorder called tinnitus. I was surprised, I'd had it so long that I thought it was normal. This is all in hindsight now, but we should have picked up that these "symptoms" may have been signs of a problem brewing in the background. Lesson learned: lifestyle changes shouldn't be just dismissed out of hand.

When we closed the practice, we wanted to make it as smooth a transition as possible for our patients. There was also a professional obligation to do so. We used guide lines from the College of Physicians and Surgeons and also consulted colleagues had already gone through process of closing their practice. The College's guideline was to put a public notice in the office notifying patients that the practice was closing in ninety days. In addition to putting up a public notice in the office, I made thousands of phone calls notifying our patients of the closure. We were not obligated to find a new doctor for our patients, but we found five doctors willing to take our patients. Also several patients were proactive and found their own doctors. Two doctors had family members of our existing patients and were willing to bring them into their practice. Two other doctors had immigrated to Canada and were building their practices and accepted thousands of our patients. One doctor wanted all of Pat's diabetic patients, which was a godsend. Diabetic patients are complicated and can require a lot of maintenance, so it was a real blessing for those patients. Many of our charts didn't have updated contact information and I was unable to reach them. For patients who had been deceased for two years or more I destroyed the chart as per guidelines.

After the practice was closed came the task of safely storing the patient charts. A couple of doctors took the entire chart so we didn't have to copy them. We drew up a simple agreement that, in the event we needed a patient chart, they would give us access to them. This helped us a lot in storage and the cost of chart copies. One of Pat's colleagues went so far as to make complete duplicates of these patient charts when he closed his practice. That was at a cost of ten thousand dollars and that was an expense we were not willing to pay. The medical society required doctors to keep patient charts for ten years and for children the rule was ten years or to the age of twenty-one whichever was longer. Some doctors didn't follow these rules at all. They would give their patient three months to come pick up their chart, after which they destroyed them. Every four months or so I would purge the charts with the medical society's guidelines and the volume of charts slowly declined. When we moved out of the community, we kept them storage for another year and I finally purged all the charts except for Pat's clinical notes and this reduced the size of our chart storage dramatically. If we needed past blood tests or imaging reports etc. we could get copies from the hospital.

We spent the Christmas holiday at home and then travelled to Philadelphia to visit my daughter for the new year. It was a much-welcomed break. We had visited them a few times before and were getting know Philadelphia and enjoyed our times there. We also had a ready-made social life just by plugging into my daughter's circle of friends. They lived in an old Irish neighbourhood called Fishtown that was becoming gentrified. The gentrification process seemed to always start with the arts community moving in first to get the ball rolling. The artists created an interesting environment that would attract development and transform an otherwise derelict area into a desirable neighbourhood. Eventually this would drive up the real estate prices, but for now Fishtown was a blend of the older established Irish families who had been there for generations and the arts community with its bohemian enclaves of art studios, coffee shops and micro breweries. It began with one coffee shop and other restaurants followed. We stayed a week before returning home. Pat had some after hours clinic shifts booked and we had to go home so she could fulfill that obligation.

Usually going north I would cross the Delaware River and get on the New Jersey turnpike to avoid going through NYC. On this trip I decided to take the I-95 and get on the turnpike further north. I missed the ramp I needed and we ended up going through NYC anyway. We were just getting off the George Washington Bridge into Manhattan when we were rear-ended. The impact was strong enough to knock my granddaughter off the back seat where she was lying down and onto the floor. Pat banged her head against the door post hard enough that she let out a howl. I wanted to stop at a hospital for her to be examined. Even if she wasn't injured, the report could be useful if an insurance claim needed to be filed. She said she would just wait to see her PCP when we got back home. When we got back home she made an appointment to see her own doctor. I asked how the appointment went. She said her doctor told not worry about the bump on the head and didn't order any investigations, no imaging, nothing. I was stunned. If a kid came to Pat's office after a hard bang on the head playing hockey, she would have ordered an investigation just make sure there were no injuries or concussion. First we had to travel to the USA to get a liver biopsy done because her gastroenterologist botched the job and now this. This was another erosion in my confidence for Pat's doctor. You may have been at a social event and her someone say something that gave you pause. I recalled her PCP flippantly say at a dinner party once that cancer is not such a bad way to die. Cancer can be a slow agonizing death. What kind of a doctor would even harbour such a notion, let alone express it? How do you think her cancer patients would respond if their doctor that thought like this? A year after we were rear-ended in NYC, a brain image revealed that Pat had a lacuna infarction in her brain just behind her right ear, the same area where she had struck her head on the car door post. Lacuna means a cleft or empty space and infarct is dead tissue. This can be caused by a lack of blood supply caused by stroke or trauma. Did the impact from being rear-ended cause the lacuna infarct? Pat's doctor never ordered a brain image at the time, so we'll never know. Pat's doctor was also our next-door neighbour's doctor. He said something that people will not say in polite company, but think it privately in their own minds. He said, "How can she tell me, her patient, to lose weight when she is much more over weight than I am?" He was an auto mechanic by trade and he went on to say that, if his personal vehicles were in bad shape or didn't run, he couldn't expect anybody to hire him to fix their vehicles. Political correctness frowns upon fat shaming; however, I'm not politically correct nor am I fat shaming. It's a fair question that, if your doctor can't take care of themselves, then what quality of care can their patients expect from them?

Pat was working about ten hours a week in the clinics. The well woman clinic was providing more than an income stream. It was providing hundreds of women in the community with much-needed health care services who didn't have a primary care physician and it meant a lot to Pat to still make a meaningful contribution. This preventative medical care was not insignificant and was a win for her and for the patients. She was starting to look more relaxed and her smiles were coming back again. Everyone noticed that she was happier and they were glad to see it. She now realized the agonizing over whether to close the practice was the right decision to take. She started getting back into exercise, attending some Pilates classes and was eager to resume some of her hobbies like photography. A nice balance between personal and professional life was starting to take shape. Hope and optimism not only adds to quality of life but can make a significant contribution to improving one's health. This new-found peace and the nice rhythmic balance between personal and professional life was all to be short-lived. In February 2009, Pat got a phone call from the head of family practice that was going to put her into eighteen months of stress that was far worse than the medical practice she just closed. She wanted Pat's billing number.

UNDER SIEGE

Hope is a continuous prayer. It streams wordlessly from the spirit.

Canada has a single-payer government-funded medical system. Although it is a federally funded program, the implementation is left to the provinces. In order for a doctor to practise medicine and get paid, they must have a government-issued billing number. In order to get a billing number, they must have hospital privileges. Each hospital in the province had their own rules that a doctor had to meet to get these privileges. The largest city in the province simply gave privileges with virtually no rules. For the hospital in our city to grant privileges, a doctor had to be in private practice, be in a call group, attend monthly meetings for their specialty and participate in committee work. Now that Pat had closed her practice, the head of family practice wanted to rescind her hospital privileges. The loss of hospital privileges would trigger the loss of her billing number. She would no longer be able to work at the after-hours clinics and her livelihood would be gone.

This was an unexpected turn of events. The seed of optimism that started to take root in Pat wilted. Colleagues who had encouraged her to take the step of closing the practice were also surprised. The drama that was to unfold over the next fifteen months would take a heavy toll on Pat. The colleagues who encouraged Pat to close her practice felt terrible and partly responsible for the trouble this brought on her.

This was a serious game changer and had the potential of completely changing the plans for our future. We were blindsided and we weren't sure how to proceed. We had made plans to take the month of March and go to Costa Rica prior to that fateful phone call and we decided to go ahead with the trip. Maybe getting away would help us to think more clearly about what to do. We had been there once before when Pat attended a Continuing Medical Education course and really enjoyed it. We booked a casita from a fellow Canadian in the little village of San Mateo. Our flight was out of Philadelphia, so we went a few days ahead of time to spend some time with my daughter again. I was hoping the trip would help get some of the peace back that Pat had gained. It didn't. Despite the beauty of Costa Rica and the warm weather, a dark cloud was hanging over both of us the entire time.

We flew into San Jose and our hosts were there to meet us. The trip had a dual purpose. In addition to rest and relaxation, it was also a scouting trip to see if we wanted to live in Costa Rica. We had always intended to move to a warmer climate with a lower cost of living. Our hosts were a retired married couple; he was Canadian and she was Costa Rican. Although the working years were in Canada, they travelled every year to Costa Rica to visit her family. They were very helpful, providing insights and practical information on what to expect living in Costa Rica. The previous trip for Pat to attend the CME was to the north-west Nicoya peninsula. We liked the arid dryness of the area, but it was a well-developed tourist destination and several celebrities were living there driving up real estate values, making it too expensive for our bank account. We intended to explore the whole country, but we never made it the Caribbean coast. We travelled quite extensively the west coast and some of the central valley. Costa Rica's highest point is Mount Chirripo at 12,536 feet so you can up and down the elevations to find the temperatures you like. There are also twelve distinct climatic zones to choose from. The village of Atenas was a good example. It is at an elevation of 700 metres and may have the perfect year round temperature ranging around 20–25°C. There was very little need for heating or cooling. The higher elevations had far fewer bugs and household appliances lasted longer away from the humid salty air down on the coast. What should have been a nice get away wasn't working for Pat. The trip had its moments, but the dread of what she might have to face when she got back home never went away. She wasn't smiling much and I was concerned too.

When we returned from Costa Rica, all was quiet. The head of family medicine made no attempts to contact Pat while we were gone. Pat decided to just let that sleeping dog lie and she resumed working clinics shifts again. The well woman clinic in particular was happy to have her back and started booking shifts for her right away. A female doctor who did pelvic exams was in demand. She tried to carry on as normal, but she was in a constant state of worry wondering when the hospital would drop the hammer again.

There was a lot of interest in Pat's case within the physician community for several reasons. The doctors who had already closed their practices and suggested for Pat to follow them in kind saw Pat's treatment as a double standard. They couldn't understand why she was being singled out this way. There were other doctors who were considering closing their practices and were watching closely how her situation would turn out before committing to the idea. They didn't want to be subjected to the same harassment. There were a couple of strategy meetings with doctors in her call group to find a solution. One of the doctors in her call group tried to defend Pat in the hospital at a family practice meeting. He had already closed his practice the year before and potentially was putting his own hospital privileges at risk by standing up for Pat. He was the only one to stand up for her because the other doctors were too afraid to join in her defence. This was a courageous attempt and we appreciated it. Most doctors, like most people, aren't willing to rock the boat to protect their own self interests. This is understandable, but many doctors at the hospital were fully aware of the creeping fascism that had taken place at the hospital over the years. It would have been in everyone's self interest to take a stand with Pat because there was no reason to think it wasn't going to get worse.

One of the physicians suggested that Pat opt out of the Canadian medical system. That suggestion was ridiculous and disingenuous. He had also closed his practice and was still provided hospital privileges. He also had the opportunity to stand up in Pat's defence at the hospital, but declined. He also knew that Pat had closed her practice for health reasons and, if she didn't have the stamina for the practice, she certainly didn't have the stamina to take on that challenge. Opting out meant that a doctor would direct bill a patient for services and there was no market for that. Opting out also meant that a doctor was totally responsible for their patient's care including any complications and emergency care. This was untenable for all intents and purposes and my belief is that it was designed that way because the Canadian single-payer medical system wants to be the only game in town. All was quiet when we returned home, but the hammer did eventually drop and it continued to drop many times over the next fifteen months.

Pat thought that doing the well woman clinic may solve the problem for hospital privileges. There were hundreds of women in the community who didn't have a primary care physician and didn't have access to this basic preventative care. Primary care physicians are the gatekeepers that patients need to go through to access secondary medical services like specialists. She was finding women with undiagnosed life-threatening conditions and was able to refer them to the services they needed. She needed to retain her hospital privileges to help these patients. This meant absolutely nothing to the hospital. They were willing to throw these patients under the bus to maintain their rigid, arbitrary rules for hospital privileges. Their position was opposite to a patient-centred medical system and didn't fulfil the spirit of universal coverage for medical care that was Canada's single-payer system mandate. However, the hypocrisy didn't stop there. Salaried doctors saw a fraction of the patients that their fee-for-service counterparts saw on any given day. The hospital still granted these salaried doctors their hospital privileges despite their failure in meeting the rising health care needs in the community. This was a shameful, hypocritical position to take that defied explanation.

Pat had gained wide-ranging experience in medicine over her twenty-five-year career and could serve in many capacities that would benefit the community. There were many areas where she could help at the hospital. All the doctors who closed their practices were accommodated to retain their hospital privileges and all only worked part time. Why were allowances made to her colleagues and not Pat? A glaring example was surgical assists. She had done surgical assists many times and was fully qualified. One of the operating units was only used for one surgery a week because lack of staff. So, there was an obvious need and would have helped clear the huge back log for surgeries. Many societies consider older generations as a repository of experience and knowledge, but our society doesn't share this opinion. Involvement of older doctors in part time work and maybe mentoring at some level could have been an addition to the system, not a burden.

The physician community was a small one and I got to know many doctors. Some I considered friends. As in any community or group, you get to hear the good, the bad and the ugly over time. In the next ensuing months, a physician's name kept coming up that I had never recalled hearing before. I had met most of the doctors through mingling at social events or tagging along with Pat to medical seminars and I was curious as to why I had never heard of him. Apparently, this guy only went to the hospital's annual award show only to claim his prize. This physician was a total self serving political operative. He had been head of family medicine in the past and when his tenure was up, he still lurked in the back ground exerting strong influence in various aspects of hospital business. For most doctors, seeing inpatients is the most stressful and disliked part of the job. A vote was taken at a general staff meeting a few years prior to have hospitalists take care of the inpatients. The doctors voted overwhelmingly in favour of having hospitalists. This was shot down by this one doctor. He was in charge of a training program for interns at the hospital and hospitalists would interfere with the program and he would lose a lucrative source of income. He also cherry picked some of the young doctors in the program and groomed them for positions in the hospital's administration. The current head of family medicine who was harassing Pat for her hospital privileges was one of his proteges. His tentacles were everywhere and he had incestuous professional relationships with many on the hospital staff. I also learned from other doctors that he was known for carrying grudges for the simplest of reasons. Our closest doctor friend went on a canoe trip with him years ago. He was experienced at canoeing from an early age and, when they encountered some white water, the guy insisted on portaging around it. Our friend just canoed right through it. This offended him and for years held a grudge over such a petty thing and had been confrontational ever since. This guy would exert payback through his influence within the hospital. The target of his wrath may not even know that their problems were originating from him because he would work behind the scenes. This is the behaviour of a sociopath. Pat recalled when she first moved to the community that he wanted her to share his practice with him, but she declined. Could this be part of the source of Pat's problem with hospital administration? His petty vindictiveness and willing to settle a score no matter how old seemed well within the realm of possibility. Anybody reading this could write me off as having sour grapes, accuse me of conspiracy thinking or just spreading gossip. You can take this for what it's worth, but everyone knows that there are people who behave like this. We have all run into them before.

The siege to rescind Pat's hospital privileges was drawn out over fifteen months. There were several meetings with the head of family practice and chief of staff to find a solution. The well woman clinic didn't meet their criteria despite the fact there were two other doctors who had closed their practice who worked the same clinic and were allowed to keep their privileges. Offering to work at the hospital in some capacity like her colleagues was refused without a reasonable explanation. We asked what was the protocol and steps that needed to be taken to close a practice and still maintain privileges. There weren't any guidelines. There didn't seem to be any consistency on how the other doctors closed their practices and still were allowed to retain their privileges. It seemed as though things were made up as they went along. The proposals that Pat offered were dismissed with no explanation or counter proposal. There never were any minutes taken for these meetings. It became apparent that there would be no resolution and they wanted her out period. Pat was getting really discouraged and demoralized. She went to a counsellor to help cope with the stress. Her counsellor said that there are always agendas at play…always. It appeared to be so with this situation, but we didn't know what it could be and why it appeared she was being singled out.

Pat was now waking up early every morning and sitting up in bed with worry and anxiety. I was really concerned if she was going to be able to tolerate what I now considered workplace bullying. She is one of the toughest and most determined people I've ever met, but her stamina was wearing down from the harassment. Some of her colleagues were worried that she might have a stroke or some other acute health issue from all this. She wavered between fear and anger as to what the future might bring. The peace and the smiles that came from closing the practice were now long gone. There have been documented suicides of doctors due to workplace harassment, from either the system or their own professional organizations. Witnessing first hand this vicious manipulation, I could understand this. Thankfully, Pat would never consider ending her life. She was more the type to call someone out to the parking lot and square off with them.

We decided to consult lawyers to see if we could take legal action.

The first problem we encountered was finding a legal firm that did not do some kind of work for the provincial government. Firms that did work for the provincial government declined to get involved, citing conflicts of interest. We found one lawyer who lived in another city that was willing to consider it and she was fully aware of the toxic environment at Pat's hospital. Another lawyer who was also the ex-minister of health for the province was willing, but in both cases they wanted huge retainers without providing any confidence in the outcome. During all of this Pat was still working at the well woman clinic and she would drop off pap tests to the lab at the hospital. She tried to slip in and out unnoticed and then one day she met another doctor who was trying to get in and out of the hospital unnoticed as well. She was a veteran emergency room physician who wanted to retire, but still wanted to do some after-hours clinics like Pat. The hospital was harassing her too. This is when I clued in that the only two doctors who were being harassed were both women.

We fully intended to move from the community, but the house needed some upgrades before we could put it on the market. An anniversary was coming up with Pat's disability insurance policy and this entitled her to a rebate of premiums for several thousand dollars. We would use this to fund the renovations. I had worked in construction for years and I would do most of the work to reduce the costs. The project was extensive, expensive and complicated. The house needed a new roof, new doors and windows, and some structural and cosmetic changes on the interior. Tackling this project would make good use of my time and the house would be ready for market. Between Pat's illness and the harassment from the hospital, the last few years were very difficult for the both of us. The situation came to a head in the spring of 2010 and as difficult as the last few years had been, it was nothing compared to the hell that would be unleashed upon her and the deep dark hole that it would put us in for the next five years.

CRUSHED, DISILLUSIONED, ANGERED

Life is after all a process of letting it all go.

Pat, you have Alzheimer's disease. WHAT? You're basing this on a thirty-minute MoCA (Montreal cognitive assessment) test? At least, that was my reaction to the news. I was accused of being in denial for even questioning the accuracy of the diagnosis. You're expecting me to believe that Pat has Alzheimer's disease based on a simple cognitive test without any further investigations? You're full of shit!

Let me turn back the clock and I'll explain how we arrived at this. During the "negotiations" for hospital privileges, Pat avoided going to the hospital and only went when necessary. She tried to keep a low profile and got out as quickly as possible. Despite this, the head of family medicine called Pat and said she was receiving reports that Pat was acting strange. She was described as being very agitated and appeared to be aimlessly wandering around. It's true that Pat wasn't her old self and the change starting during the year of harassment and got worse as the year went on. Constant bullying will wear anyone down. I and some of Pat's colleagues were very concerned how this pressure was going to affect her. A few years later, I read a book written by a Quebec doctor who had also faced harassment and his reaction was very similar to what Pat was going through: an emotional spectrum of fear, worry and anger.

The head of family medicine insisted that Pat be assessed by the hospital's in-house psychologist. If Pat wanted to retain her billing number, she had no choice when the head of family medicine had the power to rescind her hospital privileges. This was an unexpected turn of events. It came as a surprise to everyone who was following Pat's situation as well. One of the emergency doctors that she had worked with for years advised her to just walk away. With everything that happened so far, I thought his suggestion might be the wisest choice to make. I was sure this was a set-up for Pat to fail. I was also sure the hospital was making an example of her to send a message to the other physicians in the community. We had no legal advice, her colleagues weren't standing up for her, the professional organizations that she paid dues to for her entire career would not get involved or offer any advice. We were alone. Pat decided to go through with the assessment. The feisty side of Pat was seeing this as an injustice and she was digging in her heels.

The weeks leading up to the assessment were very stressful for Pat. She was vacillating between worry and anger. Pat was very familiar with the MoCA test, having administered it to her own patients many times. I was concerned about how she would perform on the test considering she was being forced to take it under duress. The day came for the test and, when she returned home, she was in a sombre mood and didn't want to talk about it. After a few weeks, Pat's primary care physician called her to make an appointment to come in for the results. In attendance was the psychologist who administered the test and he wasted no time in telling Pat she had Alzheimer's disease. My cynicism for the test never expected this result. The hospital's administration wanted her billing number and were employing dirty politics to accomplish that task, but Alzheimer's disease? I didn't know any thing about Alzheimer's disease, but it was going to take more than a thirty-minute MoCA test that didn't require any training to administer to convince me. MoCA is merely a screening tool that might warrant further tests and/or investigations if there was indication of a problem. A simple urinary tract infection can cause short-term cognitive impairment, but even this wasn't ordered. Pat had no family history of Alzheimer's disease, nor was she asked if there was any.

Pat and I sat there quietly while the hospital's psychologist went over the test results. He provided an anecdotal story of another doctor who had been diagnosed with AD. A surgeon who carved his initials into a patient's liver during an operation. I was thinking, are you serious? So what did the rest of the staff in the operating room do, compliment him on his artwork? This meeting was ridiculous. I turned to Pat and she looked distraught and beaten. I asked Pat's doctor if we could speak to her. The psychologist took his cue and left. As soon as the door closed, Pat's doctor turned and said something I'll never forget, "Pat, you have Alzheimer's disease and don't even try to do anything to help yourself." I was momentarily stunned. I wasn't sure if I had just heard her correctly. What kind of a doctor would say this to a patient? My next emotion after being rattled was rage. I wanted to hit the roof, but I didn't. I kept my cool and calmly said I wasn't buying into this. I may have suppressed my anger, but she sure didn't. She leaned forward and slammed her hands on her knees and said I was in denial. This was the second time that one of Pat's doctors got angry. What is going on here? First you tell Pat not to help herself and now you're getting angry?

Pat's primary care physician was more than her doctor she and Pat were friends. They shared the same call group for twenty years. They both did obstetrics and had covered each other many times over the years and this is how you now treat her? I knew her for fifteen years myself and would never have expected this reaction. I pointed out that Pat was taking the test under duress and it could have affected her performance. She said that was irrelevant. I am a musician and I've had stage fright many times, not being able to perform pieces of music I could play in my sleep. She knew that Pat's entire career was at stake. She then suggested that Pat's "strange" behaviour may have been a complication of her hemochromatosis. I thought to myself, now, wait a minute, if you think hemochromatosis is the underlying problem, then why are you diagnosing her with Alzheimer's disease? That's two different diseases; which one is it? The treatment plan for AD was sure to involve powerful drugs with serious side effects. No matter how I looked at it, this whole thing was spiralling into insanity and she is telling me that I'm the one in denial. The last thing she said was it was a shame that Pat had been diagnosed with AD because "you're so pretty". That really creeped Pat out.

Over the year, Pat had progressively become withdrawn and was not herself. She was getting more fatigued due to illness, but I knew that she was getting very disheartened directly due to the harassment. The hospital would never see it this way, let alone admit it. It was a big mistake for Pat to agree to this assessment and she should have just walked away. Her own doctor/friend/colleague was also very politically connected and for her to tell Pat to not question the diagnosis was very suspect. Removing any sense of hope for a patient is contrary to good doctoring. I wasn't accepting any of this at face value. I was now wondering what the real status of Pat's health issues was now that her health care had been corrupted by the political agenda of the hospital. It was hard to believe that this is how the hospital saw fit to end her career. One thing was for sure: they now could rescind her hospital privileges and get her billing number. Pat's career was finished.

As we were walking through the parking lot from her doctor's appointment, I told Pat not to buy into this. In the last few years we had been battling Pat's health issues and the hospital administration and in both cases her medical community failed her. She was now wondering if she did indeed have Alzheimer's despite the credibility of a diagnosis based on a simple cognitive screening tool and the political motivation behind it. She had worked with these people for her entire career and didn't know what to think. I knew that she was rattled and experiencing a cognitive dissonance on how the hospital and her colleagues could be so vicious that they would use a phony diagnosis just to get her billing number. In that moment, the beat down was complete.

What a mess! Looking back, it all seems surreal and it is hard to believe this had all occurred. When I recounted these events to people, no one believed us. The medical/industrial complex is impressive. Hospitals are imposing structures and are a physical focal point in a lot of communities. Hospitals are filled with expensive, complicated equipment that takes training to operate. They are beehives of activity with patients and visitors coming and going. Medical schools are equally impressive and a medical degree bestows upon doctors a status that is held in high regard in the communities they serve. I live in Canada, with its government single-payer medical system, which to many Canadians is a source of national pride and to even question its effectiveness will bring scorn down upon you. This unquestioning, blind faith extended to our immediate family. They were fully aware of the political agenda of the hospital and the underhanded tactics that they were using. Yet, they readily accepted the diagnosis of Alzheimer's disease. The only help they were willing to offer was to help select a nursing home for her. Why would anybody abandon their own common sense to someone just because they had a medical degree? My father would say that he would listen to anyone, but at the end of the day he made up his own mind. Against this backdrop, I was considered the voice of a wild man in the wilderness. The admiration and respect I gained for physicians just didn't roll back to square one; it went into negative territory. My trust for physicians was now gone.

The battle to save Pat's career was over and the hospital got what they wanted. As much as I considered this an injustice, I was relieved that it was over. When Pat decided to close the practice on December 24, 2008, I was ready to leave medicine behind and reinvent ourselves with a new life. When all the kids were gone, our future was a blank slate for exploring many possibilities. Pat on the other hand never intended to completely give up medicine. She liked practising medicine; she just couldn't do it full time anymore. She was hoping that she could continue to do light-duty medicine where ever we moved to. One option was to do volunteer work. We were interested in travelling and volunteer work could mesh with that desire. There were so many places in the world that severely lacked medical services and serving there could really make a difference. We had visited a few places in Central America and the Caribbean. There was an organization called Floating Doctors based out of Panama that served remote communities. Now that the hospital had ended her career with a diagnosis of Alzheimer's disease, she would never be able to practise medicine anywhere again. Pat grieved for the loss of her career. This just added to the stress of the last few years dealing with her health and professional issues. I didn't expect this and the grief lasted for well over a year. It was a shame that we couldn't have left the community earlier so that the professional troubles could have been avoided. Unfortunately it would be another long, difficult three years before we were able to move.

Now that the hospital fiasco was behind us, it was time to refocus our attention on getting accurate assessments for Pat's health so that we knew what we were up against. For the time being there was no where else to turn, but to the same medical system that had let Pat down medically and professionally. The line between a politically driven diagnosis and actual diagnoses had become so blurred that it was difficult to tell where one started and the other ended. In addition to workplace harassment, she had also received poor medical care and neither was acceptable.

A few weeks after Pat was informed she had Alzheimer's disease, she received notification that a Spec CT of her brain was ordered and an appointment was made to see a neurologist at the memory clinic in Halifax. The brain scan was going to be done at the hospital and the radiologist doing the scan was one of her classmates from medical school. Pat could only go on faith that his interpretation wouldn't be tainted by the politics. I thought that it shouldn't matter where the scan was done or who did the imaging. I wasn't aware at the time that imaging could have a wide divergence of interpretations. Pat had a high regard for the memory clinic in Halifax. She had sent several of her own patients there over the years and knew their work well. The memory clinic was in an entirely different province and should be free from the politics back home. We had to wait five months for the brain scan and seven months for the memory clinic appointment. Long wait times is typical in the Canadian single-payer medical system.

While waiting for these appointments, I had time to review what had happened. I needed to gain enough understanding of medicine to know what I should expect, but more importantly that I could trust the medicine that Pat would be receiving. Passivity in the face of a problem just creates anxiety for me. I didn't have a medical degree, but I am pretty good at zeroing in the right questions to help me understand what I need to know. I am a fan of hard science. Hard science essentially strives to reveal hard truths about our world. One hard truth leads to another truth, all leading to solutions to make our lives for the better. The perception of medicine is that it is scientific and evidence-based. If that is so, then why would there be any need for a second opinion? Hard science is not an opinion. Medicine and human biology is far too complicated to think of it like the hard sciences we learned in high school or university. Medicine may apply some hard sciences, but the practice of medicine itself is very much an intuitive art form and comparing medicine to hard sciences is too simplistic.

Profiling and standard of care has taken over much of "doctoring". This is subverting the doctor/patient relationship. I admire and respect science, but I also respect experience and a refined intuitive sense. Good doctoring is a blend of these two and eliminating one will only degrade the quality of medicine. Not everything is science; indeed, a lot of good science started with a hunch. Profiling takes an individual patient out of the equation and standard of care encourages group think. Doctors used to talk to their patients and sometimes could tell a lot just by looking at them. Now sometimes doctors spend more time looking at their computer screens than observing their patients. This is the direction that medicine is going in and graduates of medical schools are trained to think this way. As the older generation of doctors retire, their way of practising medicine could be lost. In my opinion, medical schools have swung the pendulum too far in the pursuit of scientific/evidence based medicine and lost some of its soul. As I gained understanding of medicine and Pat's issues in particular, there were too many medical loose ends for me to feel comfortable with.

After I realized that the medical science was on shaky ground, I started having a closer look at medical practitioners. Through Pat I knew a lot of doctors. We had a few doctors in our extended family as well. I knew that a medical degree and higher education in general do not equate to a higher level of wisdom. What is important is critical thinking and problem-solving skills. I quickly found out that titles and letters after your name didn't guarantee that. The only difference between a plumber and a doctor are different skill sets and that's about it. By making this comparison I am not trying to disregard the higher responsibility of medicine. The point that I'm trying to make is that a lot of medicine can be understood without having a medical degree. For me this was empowering and helped me make more informed decisions in Pat's health care. Maybe if more people got involved in their health care it could also improve the system. Everyone knows someone who has a chronic unresolved health issue. One of Pat's colleagues was a career emergency room doctor and he said easily half of the diagnoses in the emergency room were wrong. I can't think of another service that would be able to get away with this level of non-performance. The Canadian single-payer medical system has struggled for years trying to maintain a level of care. A public health system should involve the public. Yet the public are the only stakeholders who are not involved or held to account. I think that the public should not only be involved but held to account to a defined responsibility. I know some doctors who would welcome more patient involvement and responsibility in their health care. It is also true that some doctors would find this inconvenient. Blind faith in the medical system can enable a free pass for failures and mediocrity. Excellence and results need to be demanded from all stakeholders or the system will never rise to the potential that patients and health care workers deserve.

Being told I was in denial about the AD diagnosis persistently nagged me in the back of my mind. I told this to one of the doctors who was one of our biggest supporters. He told me, unless a doctor is willing to move in with a patient, doctors depend on the insights and feedback from family members. This brings up the controversy of anecdotal information versus medical science. Researchers are particularly dismissive of anecdotal information. They contend the answer to lack of science is more science. That's fine and dandy, but that is not the reality of clinical work and is ridiculous for two reasons. First, a doctor implements a course of treatment for a patient and on subsequent appointments the doctor asks how the patient is doing. Hello, that's anecdotal information! To not consider a patient's experience is arrogant and an example of the bubble that doctors confine themselves to. Doctors may only receive a few hours of lecture in medical school on some issues that patients live with for years. So who is the expert? In the end, people believe what the want to believe. I felt I didn't have that luxury because we needed to resolve Pat's issues regardless of what we believed. We had to go where the results took us. It's not easy trying to maintain sober second thoughts when someone is so personally close to you, but I had to. There was too much at stake. The up coming appointments were months away, but I was glad that investigations were started.

I didn't know anything about AD, but I would get to know a lot about it over the next few years. I would even get to know more about it than some of her primary care physicians: their words not mine. This may sound like I'm making myself out as an expert, but it's more of a statement how little mainstream medicine knows about this disease and it doesn't take much to blow by them. I also didn't realize how this diagnosis ostracized you from everyone including family. I became so jaded that I wondered if the hospital had diagnosed her with AD to not only get her billing number but to sabotage our life going forward. At first I thought my naivety was in thinking that Pat would get an honest unbiased assessment. I was wrong; it went deeper than that. Try to find a doctor who may arrive at a different diagnosis in this single-payer medical system. Their paychecks came from the same place and they knew this could open up a world of grief that could threaten their livelihoods. This conclusion would only come later and it wasn't made in a vacuum, but for good reason. For now we proceeded with the investigations as ordered.

THIS IS MEDICINE?

Maybe the trick
is to just breathe...
so I've been told.
The rhythm of in and then out
is one of the essences that we
experience in this life.
It's good to return to an essence
once in a while...
don't you think?
Just... breathe.

Pat had left her doctor's office with an Alzheimer's diagnosis, completely disheartened. She only became more demoralized in the months leading up to the investigative appointments. I didn't think of it at the time, but a family meeting should have been made with her doctor to talk this over. This may have applied some transparency to the shenanigans that the hospital and her doctor were up to. Even though the family were aware of the dirty politics at the hospital, they wouldn't have been interested in an appointment anyway. For reasons I'll never understand, the family capitulated to the Alzheimer's diagnosis. We were alone and the hospital knew it. I tried as best as I could to keep Pat's spirits up, with little success. For now, I would keep working on the house getting it ready for when we were ready to put it on the market.

Now for the investigations, first up Spec CT. On November 26, 2010, Pat had a Spec CT done by a radiologist who was classmate of Pat's at med school in consultation with a nuclear medicine specialist in Halifax. Single photon emission computed tomography composes a 3-D image of the brain. She was given an injection of technetium (a radiopharmaceutical) to observe the blood perfusion. The results "appeared" to show generally decreased cortical perfusion in both hemispheres of the brain. The examination also showed "some degree" of cortical brain atrophy not significantly outside the range for a brain of that age. I have placed quote marks around a couple of words as examples of the language that I learned to pay attention to over time. So far, to back up a simple cognitive test for Alzheimer's disease, we have an image result that "appears" to "some degree" to "suggest" AD or potentially Lewy body dementia. Lewy body dementia is the second most common type of progressive dementia after AD and involves protein deposits in nerve cells impairing thinking, memory and motor control.

After the imaging and report had been completed, Pat went to the radiology department and spoke to the radiologist. He said he had no experience in nuclear medicine and really couldn't comment on it. He suggested that she call the nuclear medicine specialist in Halifax. She called him up and he invited her to come to Halifax anytime and he would be willing to meet with her and go over the results. We booked an appointment a couple of weeks later and drove the two and half hours to Halifax.

We told the staff at the nursing station that we had an appointment with the nuclear medicine specialist and to let him know we had arrived. We waited four and half hours. When we finally got to go see him, the helpful attitude that he had had on the phone was gone. He was anything but accommodating. Radiologists work in dark rooms looking at images all day. His room was so small I stood out in the hall and listened in the conversation between him and Pat. He didn't have the images available for Pat to review. He sounded impatient and annoyed. He really had nothing to say that was enlightening. We spent five hours of driving time and a four-and-a-half-hour wait for a half hour consultation and gained nothing.

The next appointment was with the Memory Clinic in Halifax. I didn't know anything about them, but Pat held them in high regard and I was expecting a professional thorough investigation. She was seen by two neurologists, preceded by another MoCA test administered by a geriatric intern. The neurologists started by establishing some basics: Pat was a non-smoker and a non-drinker, there was no family history for dementia or other neurological issues, her blood pressure was normal and the air entering and exiting her lungs was normal. This was followed with an interview with some questions directed to me. They were trying to ascertain if there were any observable changes in her behaviour. We started by giving some of her health history. We explained that she started getting very tired in late 2007, which was attributed to fatigue due to hemochromatosis. Although she loved medicine, she made the difficult decision to close the practice on December 24, 2008. In addition to fatigue, she was very concerned about her cirrhotic liver becoming cancerous and worried quite a bit about it. After the practice was closed, some of our closest friends and I noticed almost immediate results. She looked less stressed, smiled more, enjoyed her clinic shifts and had more energy. After we had some of this background for context, we also explained the troubles with the hospital administration and the effect it had on her. I told the neurologists that Pat started having a stammer around the end of 2009. Along with the stammer she was having some memory slips and occasionally having trouble finding words or using word replacement in conversation. Anxiety seemed to be a cofactor because these issues increased in stressful situations. Conversely, the speech problem all but disappeared when she was relaxed. There was no problem with writing. I asked the neurologists if iron overload from the hemochromatosis could have affected her brain.

My question went unanswered. It would be four years later that an American hospital would investigate that possibility.

After the interview, mental tests were conducted in six categories: cranial nerves, motor, sensory, reflexes, cerebellar and stance/gait. The cranial nerve test was a funduscopy examination that checked the back of the eye. Her visual fields were full, pupils equal in size and reacted to light normally. The cranial nerve exam was normal. The motor exam showed no signs of a movement disorder. Her muscle tone was normal and symmetrical. The sensory test had a slight irregularity. There was a slight decrease in detecting vibration in her big toes. The pin prick test was intact and symmetrical throughout. She was tested for graphesthesia, sense of touch. She was tested for stereognosis, which is the ability to identify objects by touch only. She was given a Romberg test, being able to stand with eyes closed. Failure of the graphesthesia, stereognosis, and Romberg tests would have indicated damage associated with the parietal lobe of the brain. These tests were normal, although the Spec CT of her brain showed that the parietal lobe had some blood perfusion problems. The reflex test showed some hyperreflexia (exaggeration of reflexes) on her right side. The cerebellar test had her touching her nose with her index finger and reaching out to touch the end of a ball point pen. The result was no dysdiadochokinesia (the ability to perform these movements).

I want to take a moment here to point out that words with eighteen letters in them and difficult to pronounce is why many people are intimidated by medicine and consider doctors to have a knowledge that is far above the patient's ability to understand. Unfortunately, medicine is riddled with technical terms like this and you will need to sort through it when you get involved in your health care. Patience, persistence and a good dictionary will get you through. This kind of language is a holdover from medical academia when it was driven by a pure science and truth. The medical system can be best described now as a medical/industrial complex. I am pro business, but business interests can conflict with what is best for the patient. Confounding patients to think that understanding medicine is beyond their reach serves the industrial side of the medical/industrial complex very well. It will be confusing to discern if the medicine you receive is patient driven or business-driven when it comes to doing your due diligence, but you will need to for clear-eyed assessments for your medical care. I approach medical services like I do any other service and it's buyer beware.

The final impressions and recommendations of the neurological report was there were irregularities of a global nature most prominently in the posterior parietal lobe. Their conclusion was Pat had atypical Alzheimer's disease and they wanted further investigations. An MRI of Pat's brain was ordered and they started Pat on a trial of a cholinesterase inhibitor for Alzheimer's disease. Cholinesterase is a chemical messenger in the brain and research showed in AD brains there is a decrease in the chemical and this drug could boost its performance. They also prescribed the Alzheimer's drug Exelon because it was the least taxing on Pat's damaged liver. Pat had been previously taking Effexor for depression and the neurologists wanted her to restart this prescription. They also wanted her to be followed by a neurologist back in our hometown.

Pat stopped taking Effexor because she felt it didn't help at all. Effexor is a selective serotonin and norepinephrine reuptake inhibitor (SNRI) that acts upon the neurotransmitters serotonin and norepinephrine that are naturally present in human brains. These drugs operate on the theory that mental disorders are caused by chemical imbalances in the brain. There never has been a diagnostic test to clearly and consistently confirm a chemical imbalance as the root cause of brain dysfunction. Patients are prescribed these drugs on a trial and error basis until a perceived result is attained. These drugs can make adaptive changes to the brain that oppose their intended use. Neurotransmitters travel across the synapses in the brain to a binding site. Think of it like a lock and key where a specific key fits a particular lock. Interfering with neurotransmitter function can deform the receptor sites so that the neurotransmitter is unable to bind to it's receptor site. For this reason its recommended for a patient to taper off these drugs because stopping abruptly may result in permanent receptor damage. In other words, brain damage. Doctors follow manufacturers' guidelines for tapering, which can be too quick for many patients. Adverse effects from a quick taper are never attributed to the drug, but to the patient's under lying depression. The doctor then puts the patient back on the drug at an increased dosages, further compounding the problem. This creates a needless, vicious cycle of dependency. Tragically, patients are unaware of these issues and believe they are getting sicker instead of going through a drug withdrawal. It's heart breaking that they blame themselves.

Some of the side effects of depression drugs are nervousness, constipation, anxiety, insomnia and seizures. Many patients are prescribed another drug for each of these symptoms, poly-drugging the patient with little or no consideration on how these drugs will interact with each other. Some symptoms seizures – for example – are considered rare. Medical science knows very little about the brain, by their own admission. To make a claim that a symptom is rare is baseless, in my opinion. There is no test to determine if an individual could be the rare exception. SNRIs and SSRIs can reduce the serotonin levels in the prefrontal lobe even at low doses. Serotonin abnormalities have been documented in all three forms of dementia. The low serotonin levels are attributed to the dementia and not attributed to the drug the patient may be on. Moreover, serotonin has effects beyond the brain, influencing growth, repair, and function of tissues in the body outside the brain. Thirty years of research has shown that patients treated with psychotherapy had better outcomes than those who were prescribed drugs for treating depression. To prescribe a drug that interferes with the natural functioning of the brain's own neurotransmitters is reckless and irresponsible.

The MRI was done on March 7, 2011, and the report was eight

lines long. Those eight lines took me several hours to process. Without a medical background, I had no idea what to look for, so I looked at everything. The first two lines read, "The examination consisted of a sagittal T1-weighted sequence, axial T2-weighted and T2 weighted FLAIR sequences and an axial diffusion weighted sequence". The sagittal plane is a vertical slice of the brain from front to back. The axial plane are horizontal slices of the brain. T1 images use short TR (repetition time) and TE (time to echo), while T2 use longer TR and TE. Weighting refers to the colour of the observed fluid: TI is dark and T2 is bright. T2 weighted FLAIR means that the TR and TE are longer. Diffusion weighted sequence is used to detect water protons. Got it…now ignore it! To arrive at an understanding of medicine, you will need to learn to learn what's important and throw away the rest. It will take time, but you will learn how to cut to the chase for what is important. The report said that there was slightly more brain tissue atrophy for her age and no mass lesions were seen. This was significant to me because the neurologists at the memory clinic said the only way to definitively say that a patient had AD was from an autopsy performed after death and if it revealed a brain had severe lesions and atrophy then the patient is said have AD. This would be an important benchmark for me to watch for with subsequent brain imaging. However in 2015, a neurologist said he had many patients who had severe atrophy and lesions and that did not have AD. So the benchmark of lesions and atrophy was useless? What was I supposed to do with two opposing opinions? The MRI indicated no hydrocephalus (water on the brain), which could cause swelling. The MRI did show a lacuna (empty space) in the same area where Pat had hit her head when we got rear-ended coming off the George Washington Bridge in NYC.

There are ten warning signs for Alzheimer's disease from the Canadian Alzheimer's Society. Memory loss affecting day to day abilities: Pat's high anxiety due to workplace bullying could easily be attributed to what appeared to be memory loss at times. Difficulty performing familiar tasks like preparing meals: Pat could cook, but a smoke and water damage crew was almost needed to be called in to clean up the kitchen after she was done. Problems with language: yes, she had developed a stammer and used word substitution some times. Disorientation in time and space: this was not one of Pat's problems. Impaired judgment: nine out of ten people would approach a problem roughly the same way but Pat would be that one in ten that would go about it differently, but still arrive at the same result and sometimes a better result. So, impaired judgment? No. Problems with abstract thinking like using a calculator: Pat loved technology like PDAs, computers and cell phones, but was clueless on how to use most of these devices. The exception was her feature-heavy digital camera. She got quite adept at using the camera. Misplacing things, that's a laugh. Every morning before going to the office was panic time trying to find the car keys. Her daughters were just as bad: I found a hair brush in the freezer once. Changes in mood and behaviour: Pat could unleash a temper on occasion and the frequency of her temper flare-ups were up a bit. Changes in personality like paranoid and threatened: she was constantly worried about her cirrhotic liver and this changed her. She liked to laugh and had a happy-go-lucky attitude, which had all but disappeared. Loss of initiative: after she closed the practice she started getting interested in photography and exercise again, so I would have to say no. Pat's lifestyle reduced the risk for developing brain health issues. She always was physically active, didn't smoke or drink and ate a well-balanced meals. Her weight was always in her recommended range and went for annual physical check-ups and blood work. Nobody in her family had dementia and there were no other reasons for her to be in a risk category for Alzheimer's disease.

These are some of the symptoms for anxiety: uneasiness, fear, sleep problems, not being able to stay still, nervousness, trouble concentrating and obsessive worry, and gastrointestinal problems. These are some of the symptoms for depression: sad and anxious, helplessness, irritable, loss of interest in activities, loss of energy, disturbed sleep, trouble concentrating or focusing, remembering and making even small decisions. There are several contact points where anxiety and depression overlap and some of these symptoms can be attributed to Alzheimer's disease.

When anxiety becomes chronic then it is diagnosed as generalized anxiety disorder (GAD). I knew that Pat was experiencing a sustained anxiety worrying about her liver becoming cancerous. She had the symptoms for GAD as defined by the Mayo Clinic: difficulty handling uncertainty, indecisiveness, inability to relax, always keyed up, having a hard time concentrating, trouble sleeping, gut problems and irritability. It's not rocket science to understand how chronic anxiety can interfere with your life. Anxiety sucks up energy, interrupts clear thinking and can sideline your normal self. Could Pat's speech stammer have been caused by GAD? I know that I sometimes stammer in tense situations and in turn the stammering increases the anxiety. However, stammering could be a sign of a neurogenic issue. Pat had known liver damage from hemochromatosis and I continued to wonder if the iron deposits had damaged her brain.

Depression can be debilitating. A lot of people have experienced depression at times during their life. Prolonged and persistent depression is classified as major depression. Major depression induced by a chronic illness adds to an already existing problem. Enduring pain, compromised lifestyle and an uncertain future will wear down stamina and hope given enough time. Impaired cognitive performance, decreased memory and difficulty making decisions are some symptoms that have been attributed to depression. Brain imaging of depressed patients have shown abnormalities the hippocampus of the brain and the prefrontal cortex responsible for planning and higher executive function. Studies have shown that these areas of the brain worsen over time with patients who have major depression versus non-depressed patients.

The above symptoms and brain abnormalities have also been attributed to Alzheimer's disease. Alzheimer's patients have been known to develop depression and depression has been known to contribute to the development of Alzheimer's disease, making an accurate diagnosis difficult to ascertain. Brain and behaviour disorders are spectrum diseases and are also dynamic within the spectrum. Incorrect diagnoses can lead to prescribing the wrong drug, unnecessarily exposing a patient to its serious side effects. Patients can self-fulfill an incorrect diagnosis, simply believing it. On the other hand, treating a patient with a drug or treatment for an incorrect diagnosis can provide a false sense of hope. Most people including myself have experienced garden variety anxiety and depression in our lives. My experience is that depression and anxiety go hand in hand and can create a feedback loop. The point I'm trying to make is to pigeonhole diagnoses strictly into one issue is not only incorrect; it can lead to incorrect therapies, compounding a patient's problem. Never abdicate your common sense to the opinion of medical professionals and a medical system.

One of the symptoms of Alzheimer's disease is depression and depression can cause Alzheimer's disease. This is like what came first, the chicken or the egg? How could the original MoCA test be capable of determining which condition that a patient may be experiencing? The AD symptom that scares most people is the inability of a sufferer to be able to recognize themselves or their family. Pat has never manifested this tragedy to this day. At the end of the appointment with the memory clinic, one neurologist said something that astounded me. He said we don't know very much about Alzheimer's disease and we don't know for sure if anyone has it. Then how can you diagnose it let alone treat it? What if your diagnosis is incorrect and the treatment could cause further harm? Over time trying to resolve Pat's medical issues would turn into a monumental task. I didn't know much about medicine at this appointment, but I would get to know a lot more than these guys did. This appointment created more questions than it answered…this is medicine?

THE LAST STRAW

A lie cannot exist without the truth it's based upon

Before returning home after the memory clinic appointment, we paid a visit to Pat's youngest daughter, who was living in Halifax. In conversation, she mentioned the mother of one of her friends had been diagnosed with dementia thirteen years ago. Since the diagnosis, she showed no signs of symptoms and was living her life normally. This was an interesting piece of anecdotal information coming so shortly after the memory clinic appointment. How could someone who had been diagnosed with dementia thirteen years ago not develop any symptoms? When we got back home Pat was more demoralized than ever. Once again she was being counseled to accept an Alzheimer's diagnosis. She knew there were good reasons to doubt the diagnosis, but was worried anyway. What if they were right? We tried to restore some normalcy to our daily lives without much success. It was now a few months since Pat had to leave medicine and it didn't look like the grieving period was going to end any time soon. It almost appeared to me that she was grieving the loss of her career more than the loss of her father a few years earlier. She was a real daddy's girl and losing him was really hard on her. Many mornings I would roll over in bed around 5am only to find her already sitting up staring out the window. I tried to console her as best as I could, but she was only sinking further into depression.

The first thing Pat did when we got back home was to take out the *Compendium of Pharmaceuticals and Specialties*. This was a big blue book about three inches thick that she referred to several times a day for the side effects of drugs to help her choose the right prescription for her patients. Exelon was the Alzheimer's drug that the neurologists prescribed and the listed side effects were joint pain, sleep problems, nausea and severe stomach and abdominal pain. She already had trouble with intestinal problems and decided not to take it. I supported her decision. The memory clinic wanted Pat to be followed by a neurologist of her choice. Pat mentioned the name of a neurologist that she had worked with in the past. She liked him and, although he had moved to an adjacent province, he was close enough for him to take over Pat's care. At the mention of his name, the two neurologists belittled him because his approach was "unorthodox". I would learn in time that any doctor that was described as an "out of the box thinker" was some one that I should talk to because the most beneficial treatments for Pat would eventually all come from outside mainstream medicine. A few more weeks went by and Pat told me she had been taking the Exelon prescription. She said it seemed to be alright and she would continue to take it. I supported that decision too.

Six weeks after the memory clinic appointment in Halifax, Pat's PCP called her in for a follow-up appointment. The appointment was short and sweet. Her doctor was fixed on the Alzheimer's diagnosis and there was nothing else to discuss. She would treat her according to established protocols. She told Pat that she would make a referral for Pat to see a geriatrician instead of a neurologist. Less than a week after the appointment with her PCP, Pat woke up around 5am with a severe panic attack and was sweating profusely. I spent some time trying to settle her down and then Pat revealed to me that her PCP took it upon herself to triple the dosage of Exelon. This was a tipping point for me and the last straw I was willing to tolerate. Up until this point, my role was supportive and I was passive in getting involved in medical decisions. Medicine was Pat's wheelhouse not mine, but now I was going to get involved. My first decision was refusing to take Pat to the emergency department of the hospital where she had worked and I took her to the other hospital in town instead. The emergency room physician took routine vitals and asked what had happened. I told him I suspected these symptoms were due to tripling the dosage of the Exelon she had been taking. He looked at me and asked me who diagnosed her with AD. I explained that Pat was a physician herself and the in-house psychologist at the other hospital diagnosed her with AD based on a MoCA test. He shook his head and walked away. Pat eventually settled down and we went home. This was the end of the Exelon trial and it was the end of her primary care doctor. I told Pat she needed a new doctor and she offered no pushback because she knew it had to be done. We had some extended family members who were doctors and they were able to find Pat a new primary care doctor.

My next step was researching Alzheimer's drugs. I was dumbfounded when I learned that most dementia drugs use the same biological mechanisms as pesticides and nerve agents. The long-term and delayed brain injuries of nerve agents have been well studied by toxicologists in the military. The military also has well-developed treatment plans for military personnel who had been exposed to these poisons. On the other hand, dementia drugs are administered by trial and error. It is incredible that a drug that has the same lethal potential as nerve agent weapons are being administered so haphazardly. For millennia the starting point for a physician to practise medicine was to "first do no harm". This was a complete abandonment of that credo. It would seem to me in this instance the best way they could live up to "do no harm" was to do nothing at all.

Over the years I heard some gossip of shady activities at the hospital, but they always sounded like exaggerations to me. Not anymore. An example of this made national news headlines in 2019. It came to light that a nurse had I given several pregnant women oxytocin to induce labour without informing the patient or obstetricians. It was discovered she secretly injected the drug into saline bags with a syringe needle. In one case, the baby's heart rate dropped to a dangerously low level and an emergency C-section had to be done. The women who were involved started a class action lawsuit that included the hospital for negligence. The hospital knew that they had a far higher average of C-section deliveries, but failed to investigate. Although this made national headlines, there were several other serious issues that never saw the light of day. The staff were fully aware of problems and did nothing to bring them to anyone's attention.

Pat's new doctor was younger than Pat. Although they had never met, she had admired Pat as an older female doctor role model. She wasn't given a heads-up about why Pat needed a new doctor, so we explained the emergency room visit from the dosage increase of Exelon. We also explained because of the troubles at the other hospital that it would be best for Pat to go elsewhere. She adopted the hemochromatosis protocol that was in place for managing Pat's liver and made appointments for a hematologist and a geriatrician. At the very first appointment, the hematologist questioned if Pat had hemochromatosis. The genetic mutations for the disease were in Pat's chart. Didn't he review her chart before the appointment? Also in Pat's chart were her high iron levels at the time of diagnosis and the liver damage from the iron overload. Pat was being followed by the liver transplant surgeon in Halifax and we felt it wasn't necessary for him to be in the loop, so we fired him after the third appointment. The geriatrician wanted Pat to continue the Exelon prescription despite our concerns about the drug. Pat's new PCP told the geritrician that we were considering going to the Mayo Clinic for an assessment. We said we were considering it, but money was a factor and we hadn't decided. She said if we went to the Mayo Clinic that she would drop Pat as her patient. So much for honouring the concept of a second opinion. The Mayo Clinic is world-renowned. Why wouldn't she want Pat to get assessed at the Mayo? A geriatrician is a family doctor with a bit of specialized training. There was nothing special about her, so we fired her too.

The locum doctor that covered for Pat when she had her hip replaced had an interest in alternative medical approaches. He suggested for Pat to get an assessment at an apothecary in town. Some of Pat's patients got their prescriptions filled there, but we didn't know that the pharmacist offered health assessments. The aim of his consultations was to design a custom program tailored to each patient's specific medical needs. We made an appointment with him and in addition to his recommendations he suggested that we go see a psychology professor at the local university. This turned out to be very interesting. She was a neuropsychologist with two PhDs, one in neuropsychology (language) and psychopathology, which she had earned at the University in Toulouse in France. She did post doctoral work at Boston College and was an adjunct professor at Quebec's Sherbrooke University's faculty of medicine. She also won the Chevalier de la Legion d'Honneur du President de la Republique Francaise, France's highest award honouring those in various fields of work. She also had extensive clinical experience.

We made an appointment with her and in the first thirty minutes she told Pat she didn't have Alzheimer's disease. She worked with Pat for a total of seven and half hours. Furthermore, she trained the in-house hospital psychologist who administered the initial MoCA test that diagnosed Pat with Alzheimer's disease. She said he didn't have the experience nor the training to make such a diagnosis. This only confirmed my suspicions that the diagnosis was politically driven. She sent Pat's new PCP a copy of her final six-page report with a cover letter expressing interest in working collaboratively with her for Pat's benefit. She followed up the report with a phone call to reaffirm her interest to help. In the phone conversation, Pat's doctor asked her if she was sure that Pat didn't have Alzheimer's disease. She said she was sure, but Pat's new doctor declined the offer. This was a disappointment for the psychologist, but it didn't come as a surprise.

She had experienced this uncooperative attitude in the local medical community before. We were mystified. Why would her doctor not accept help from a psychologist with these qualifications and clinical experience? I could only conclude she wasn't going to risk putting her career in jeopardy by over turning the AD diagnosis. Her paycheck came from the same single-payer medical system. So much for her responsibility to be an advocate for Pat.

While it may have been a vindication for someone with this psychologist's CV to declare that Pat didn't have Alzheimer's disease, I wondered how could she determine with certainty that Pat didn't have AD within the first thirty minutes and then spend another seven hours of testing, but could offer no explanation for Pat's speech impediment, word searching or anxiety spikes. Some times I need to sit back and let things percolate in the back of my mind for a while. She said that people with a post-secondary education, like Pat's medical degree, have a greater chance of resolving cognitive/mental issues. The theory is people who have achieved a higher education have created more synaptic connections in their brain, similar to how exercise creates more muscle mass. I thought about this, but did it really make sense? Does an increase in synaptic connections provide the ability to heal cognitive/behavioural/mental disorders? After all, what good is an increase in synaptic connectivity if it doesn't restore a person's ability to think or restore who they were as an individual? An increase in synaptic connectivity has to provide more than pathways for a little Pac-Man to be able to run around in circles in a person's grey matter.

A far better measure of a person's ability to restore brain health and their brain's synaptic efficiency is their critical thinking and problem-solving skills. I know people who do not have a post-secondary education and possess better critical thinking skills than many doctors I have met. I also had my own experiences to reference. I took the first-year sciences of calculus, physics, biology and chemistry for credits that I needed. I worked hard to pass those courses, but, once I earned the credit, it didn't take long for me to forget everything because I had no practical use for it. The old slogan "use it or lose it" is true. So could I claim I had higher cognitive reserves from having taken these courses? I don't think so. A brain stuffed with information that is lying around dormant is like a dusty old library that nobody goes to. So what? Prior to these science courses, I had been in an electronics program several years ago. My approach was to understand the material in the course. My first test result was 67, my second test result was 63 and my third was 61. Obviously, my strategy wasn't working. For the fourth test, I asked the instructor what was going to be covered in the test. I memorized twenty-five formulas and, when the clock started for the test, I took out a blank sheet of paper and wrote down all twenty-five formulas and simply matched up variables in the test question to the formulas and scored 83 on the test. I understood very little, but I got a higher mark. So in both of these examples just what synaptic connections did I make to contribute to a higher cognitive reserve? My strategy for passing the test was a better example of my cognitive abilities than what I knew about the content of the course I was taking. The idea that Pat's medical degree gave her greater cognitive capacity doesn't hold up. I once saw a meme on social media that was so true. Doctor to the patient: "Don't think that a google search is going to replace my medical degree." Patient to the doctor: "Don't think that the one-hour lecture you had medical school is going make you an expert with what I've been living with for the last twenty years."

Now let me explain why I went off into this thought exercise because it may sound like to the reader I got lost out in the weeds. We already had neurologists tell us that medical science knows very little about the brain and it is from this context that I questioned the approach the psychologist was using and what she was going to accomplish. I am not trying to pass myself off as more intelligent than an award-winning, highly credentialed psychologist, but I am the guy that takes out my wallet to pay for her services. I couldn't care less how many "letters" you have after your name, but when I pay out cold hard cash I expect results. We were seeing her to discern if Pat had any health issues and, if so, how was it going to be resolved. We weren't here to fund some esoteric study no matter how interesting it might have been. From this point of view and several hundred dollars, she produced nothing. The only value that I received is in learning how useless a highly educated person could be in serving our purposes. This may sound harsh, but it is what it is and I wasn't going to carry on with what looked like endless testing and no therapeutics in sight.

What I didn't expect was the social cost of an AD diagnosis. It virtually ostracizes you from the rest of society. The stigma that society attaches to patients diagnosed with Alzheimer's (and many other mental disorder diagnoses for that matter) drives patients to the fringes of society. This is a tragic outcome and is counterproductive for patients making a recovery. Healthy socialization is therapeutic for the brain and behavioral disorders. Patients feel ashamed of themselves, adding to the depression and anxiety that already exist. It is an incredible situation really. Doctors diagnose patients with a disease they know nothing about, not sure if a patient actually has it, prescribe poisonous drugs that exacerbate the problem and stigmatize their patients to a life of solitude, further compounding their problems. An Alzheimer's diagnosis is the total opposite of "do no harm". The medical community couldn't be ruining people's lives any more if they had planned it. Canada's public broadcaster, the CBC, reported an unsubstantiated theory from the medical community that Alzheimer's disease may be contagious. It was quickly backtracked, but this kind of loose talk is irresponsible and can drive patients and their families even further underground. My conclusion is, if you are experiencing some sort of cognitive issue or behavioral problem, the most dangerous thing you can do is seek treatment from the mainstream medical system. The tragedy is that most patients will continue to go see their doctor unaware of the danger that may be ahead of them. Much of the general public have a blind faith in the medical system. Many believe that medicine is based on hard science and therefore any utterance becomes an embedded truth in the public conscience. Even when the diagnosis is overturned, such as in Pat's case, it is impossible to shake off and patients are stuck with it. In 2015, the AD label almost led to deadly results during an emergency room visit for Pat. I will explain this event in great detail later in the book.

The research I did on Alzheimer's disease over the next four years revealed that what mainstream medicine knows about AD and brain disorders in general is all over the map. When MSM claims that dementia could have a hundred different causal factors, that only means they have no clue as to what they are talking about. MSM's research had shown there may be a possible connection between diabetes and AD. Alzheimer's may in fact be a classification of diabetes on its own. Alzheimer's and autism may be the same disease at opposite ends of the age spectrum. Alzheimer's disease can be brewing in the background and take years for symptoms to develop. The same cannot be said for autism since it's diagnosed in childhood. To claim that AD and autism could be the same disease at opposite ends of the age spectrum is ridiculous on the face of it. A Canadian study with 1800 participants using the International Classification for Diseases guidelines revealed a prevalence for dementia at 3%. The same researchers along with the same participants using psychiatry's Diagnostic and Statistical Manual of Mental Disorders guidelines for dementia had results ten times higher. Clearly the medical community has no idea what they are doing. The state of mainstream's medicine knowledge and treatments of Alzheimer's "symptoms" is a joke and would be funny if wasn't so serious. I wouldn't take my vehicle in for servicing to a shop if I was told that it may have a hundred different reasons for it not working properly. The mechanic was either incompetent or trying to con me. Servicing a vehicle is one thing, but now we were talking about Pat's health and I demand far higher certainty and results from a doctor than I do from a mechanic.

Since I am not medically trained, I would have preferred to leave her care to someone competent. I had no choice but to get involved. Ironically, the incompetence from the medical community gave me the confidence to try to tackle Pat's health challenges. The medical system had lost my trust and I was angry. I couldn't indulge in my anger because that would just cloud my judgment and Pat's health was at stake. I had to be focused, malleable and responsive if I was to help find solutions to her health issues.

One of Pat's physician colleagues suggested for Pat to see a psychiatrist he knew in another city about an hour and half away. We decided to give the medical community one more try and made an appointment. In attendance was the psychiatrist, his nurse, and a psychiatric intern. Pat and I were interviewed separately in two different rooms before we all got together in the same room. At first it sounded good. He was going to refer Pat to the Stan Cassidy Center in Fredericton. Maybe something good could come from it where the memory clinic in Halifax had been a waste of time. However, as we related everything that happened including the bad politics at the hospital, he reclined back in his chair and his body language had skepticism written all over it. A few weeks later a letter came in the mail and he suggested that Pat go see a neurologist of her choice. He had washed his hands of it. This was the end of the road for medicine in our region. We would have to ride this out for a couple of more years before we could move. We did the best we could to get on with our lives, but living in limbo wasn't easy. We wanted to leave the area for a warmer climate, but now we had to in order to find unbiased medicine for Pat. In June of 2013, the last kid graduated high school and the house sold all in the same month and we were gone.

STEPPING OUT

Cognitive Dissonance : psychological conflict resulting from incongruous beliefs and attitudes held simultaneously

The time had finally arrived that we had been waiting so long for: we were moving away. For years we talked about turning the page and starting a new chapter in our life. We both liked to travel and experience new things. Pat had been interested in ancient Egypt and the pyramids since she was a child. She also wanted to visit Machu Picchu in the Peruvian Andes, so these destinations were high on the list. We liked dry climates and our visit to Santa Fe, New Mexico, had made a strong impression on us and we wanted to spend more time there. Pat was an art enthusiast and Santa Fe is the third largest art market in the world. Many celebrities have homes there, with some living there year around. In addition to the art market, there is a strong local music scene and touring musicians regularly coming to town. This is what interested me the most. There are several music venues including the beautiful Santa Fe Opera. An open-air concert venue with huge vistas to the west. Adding in the rich first nations culture of the south-west made Santa Fe a diverse and interesting community. There is a large annual festival celebrating native cultures, prominently featuring their artwork. The festival also invites indigenous peoples from around the world. A little farther north is Taos. It is sort of a smaller version Santa Fe, but still has its own characteristics. It also has a robust art community and is home to some nationally known musicians. We wanted a permanent home again and New Mexico was a consideration, but for now it would be fun just to travel and explore.

My daughter worked for a US airline which provided flight benefits for family members and we planned to make full use of it. There were several special interest travel blogs that we followed online and we thought, why not start our own travel blog documenting our travels using Pat's photography? Pat got a boost of confidence when a couple of art galleries in Santa Fe expressed an interest in her photography and they encouraged her to put together a portfolio for the galleries. There was also the possibility if our travel blog generated enough traffic that it could be monetized, with advertisers generating a secondary income stream for us. Another idea presented itself for my music. My daughter's regular route for the airline was to Lisbon, Portugal. Pat had travelled to Europe in her college years, but I had never been to Europe so we decided to go to Lisbon for a few weeks. My daughter would meet up with us as she flew in and out of the city during our stay. She knew the city well and served as our personal tour guide when she had layovers between flights. It was on one of these meet-ups that we joined her and her flight crew for dinner. We all went to the beautiful seaside community of Cascais and had dinner at a Brazilian restaurant right on the water. After dinner I brought out my mandolin and started playing. We were all just sitting at our tables while a generous flow of cocktails kept coming. The Brazilian staff were dancing to my Irish jigs while they were going back and forth serving us. I love Brazilians and their culture. Those people know how to ceilidh just as well as the Irish. My daughter is a much more seasoned traveller than I and she provided an insight that had never occurred to me before. She had been to that restaurant several times, but my mandolin playing provided an entirely different experience for her. She said, by playing my mandolin, I created an atmosphere that wouldn't be normally experienced by tourists. Interesting. I just took out my mandolin and played because at home it was always hard to find the time. Music was just therapeutic for me. However, there is no denying that music is a great ice breaker. We were staying in Lisbon's old section of Alfama and is full of sidewalk cafes. There was a small cafe a few short steps from our rental that we would go to and I did what I have done many times and started playing my mandolin while having a beer. Along comes a Japanese guitar player who was living in Lisbon and we started to jam. It wasn't long before a French Manouche guitar player joined us. Then along came a Romanian gypsy guitar player, two female Portuguese Fado singers, a female Russian singer and me the lone Canadian. The Japanese guy spoke English, but the others only some broken English. Musicians do not need to speak the same language to jam and to me this is the magic. Passersby would stop and listen and before we knew it we had a party. The owner of the sidewalk cafe didn't mind because the music was filling up his patio.

My daughter's observation gave me an idea. Why not leverage my music passion into a travel blog for music? Pat could video some of my musical encounters and then post it to the blog. I could provide reviews of music venues and concerts from our travels. I could also list music store locations that I found so other musician travellers knew where to get supplies. Maybe a message board feature where travelling musicians and local musicians could meet and set up music jams for themselves. I thought, if I did this right, a blog like this could easily be monetized. For the past several years I had been going to high-end guitar builders festivals. Custom-made guitars from individual guitar makers and small boutique shops were on display for purchase. Guitars selling for several thousand dollars and some well into the tens of thousands of dollars. There were many of the baby boom generation who had been amateur musicians all their lives who were now retired with time and money to indulge their music passion. This was the market that I was aiming for.

Events were moving very quickly in the last couple of weeks of

June 2013. The closing of the house sale was complete and we had to vacate by the last day of June. That deadline was coming faster than my arrangements for leaving. I was trying to thoughtfully dispose of twenty years of possessions by distributing them to our kids. They weren't interested in our hand-me-downs and in the end I rented a dumpster, parked it at the back door and filled it up. We had already moved most of the belongings that we wanted to keep to a storage unit in Halifax. After we turned over the keys to the house there were a few remaining tasks that needed to be done before we could leave town. The last three years were very stressful and staying in a hotel room for a couple days to complete arrangements proved too much for Pat and she had an anxiety meltdown. Our motel room opened onto an adjacent city park and Pat was crying and walking it off in the park. Anxiety meltdowns were not unheard of with Pat. She might have averaged one a year. Her father was calm and soft spoken, but her mother's side of the family were high strung and I guess she inherited some of that trait. The timing of the anxiety attack put me in a difficult position. The thought crossed my mind to get a prescription for an anxiety medication at an after-hours clinic, but she was too wound up to leave alone. I decided to take Pat to her daughter's place in Halifax and then I drove back for a couple of days to tidy up affairs. When I finally drove out of town, I had a sense of relief came over me like a wave. I also had a mix of apprehension for the uncertainty of our future and an excitement for the potential it held. When I got back to Halifax, Pat looked at me sheepishly and said she didn't know what to say. She was referring to her anxiety attack and I told her she didn't need to say anything. The past few years had also been difficult for me as well, but now we were past it and it was time to move on.

From the outset of this book I have advocated for people to get involved in their medical care. I believe it's a patient's responsibility to be involved. It's also prudent from the point of view of advocacy to make sure that you or your loved one is receiving proper care. There is another reason. You know who you are or you know the loved one being cared for. A patient's personality used to be a factor that doctors took into account, but now has been largely replaced with protocols that may not serve the patient. Pat had an irrational fear of death and I knew her well enough that emotional outbursts or temper tantrums at times were manifestations of this deep-seated fear.

Behavioural and mental disorders are a spectrum that defies a singular diagnosis. It is like peeling away the layers of an onion. Brain disease can cause mental and behavioural issues. Chronic anxiety can also cause brain damage. To complicate matters even further, an observed emotion like anger may not be anger but fear masquerading as anger. To sort this out requires diligent, unbiased medical sleuthing. In other words, it takes work. To neglect a deeper dive into the causes of symptoms leads to misdiagnosis and improper treatments. Treating an anxiety disorder may eliminate it as a cofactor that exacerbates another health issue and improve a patient's situation. Pat routinely went through the process of elimination in diagnosing her patients to get to the source of the problem. You don't need a medical degree to understand the soundness of this strategy. It's common sense. Doctors in the past used to take the time to get know their patients and by doing so could detect subtle changes in their patients that may require medical attention. As one doctor put it, the clinical gaze of previous generations of doctors is disappearing.

It took years for Pat had to start questioning the effectiveness of the medical treatments she was receiving. This was a difficult step for her to take since because it was forcing her to question her own career. I wasn't a doctor and rarely went to a doctor myself, so I had no frame of reference to start from. I just started thinking in general terms. If the medical system is scientific and evidence-based then why would a patient ever need a second opinion? Hard science is based on consistent reproducible results regardless of who conducts the experiment; it's not a question of opinion. How did some patients defy the odds and survive contrary to their doctor's prognosis for them not surviving?

This would seem to be a monumental miscalculation on their part. Many times they couldn't even offer a plausible explanation as to how their patient survived. If they could get this so wrong, what else are they getting wrong?

I started reading one of medicine's preeminent gold standards, the randomized clinical trial. It was common for participants in the trials to do as well or better on the placebo than the participants who were taking the drug being tested. Incredibly, some participants were fully aware that they were taking a placebo and still were healed. How could that be? Furthermore, many times the results of the placebo group were characterized as anomalies. Essentially the placebo group were being healed mind over body. It's obvious that a drug company is only interested in proving their product, but why the lack of interest by physicians in the placebo results? Their vested interests are to heal their patients. The body heals simple wounds by itself, so why not enlist the body's ability to heal itself of more serious health issues? The mainstream medical community encourages preventative medicine, but aren't they interested in being facilitators of the body's ability to heal itself? This should be their primary field of research. The answer is that the medicine is joined at the hip with the medical industry, the medical/industrial complex. The close relationship the medical industry has with the medical system has been well documented by scientific and medical journalists and their work is readily available for anybody who cares to look.

In the beginning, bringing myself up to speed on medicine was a slow and difficult task. I made good use of a medical dictionary to understand the terminology. I read imaging reports and blood test results over and over to understand them. I had no idea what to look for, so read everything in the imaging reports including the technical specs for equipment used. I looked up each of the items that were on a blood test panel. Sometimes blood test results used different units of measure than the bench marks I was comparing them to. I would have to use conversion factors so I could compare the accepted ranges to the results of Pat's tests. The research material I found on AD and dementia said there could be a hundred different sources for the disease. How could any doctor claim a definitive diagnosis of AD when there could be a hundred causes for the disease? This certainly flies in the face of medical system that prides itself for being scientific and evidence-based. This didn't make any sense. It may be useful to assign words like dementia or Alzheimer's disease for a set of symptoms, but not as a label for a specific definitive disease. I now completely dismissed Pat's AD diagnosis.

I was always frustrated that no investigations were ordered to see if Pat's brain had iron overload and possibly had been damaged. Her liver had been damaged by iron overload and it is known that other organs can have iron overload from hemochromatosis including the brain. I would come to find that mainstream medicine often ignores and even rejects its own science. Even science that they have proven to themselves with hundreds of peer-reviewed papers. Ironically, some of the complementary medical approaches have embraced these same sciences and had treated their patients successfully. We experienced this ourselves when eventually Pat would be treated by alternative practitioners. Cherry picking science is an abandonment of science. How could a medical system be so blind and closed-minded to what they had become? The irony that a medical community that had accused me of denial were in full denial themselves. Mainstream medicine is so locked up in its protocols that the system comes first and the patient second. This has resulted in failed outcomes and many times harm to the patient. There are several credible whistle blowers sounding the alarm that medical science has been compromised by business interests.

To borrow a phrase from the Gospel of Luke, "physician heal thyself", it is also important for a patient to "know thyself". Some of our personality traits and attitudes can assist us and at other times they can hinder us. Most of us only confront any short comings when compensating for them no longer is enough. Changing known bad attitudes can be difficult enough, but thoughts that we are unaware of can have a stealthy effect on our lives and health. Saint Paul expressed frustration in himself with this very thing: "I do not understand what I do. For what I want to do I do not do, but what I hate I do." Understanding who you are can be tricky business, but it is worthwhile to take stock once in a while to root out wrong thinking. Thoughts can also have an effect on the biological level as well. It was an accepted norm that genetics was hard wired, but cellular biology now knows that is not necessarily the case. Gene expression is influenced by the environment it is exposed to like the nutrients or toxins it receives. Incredibly, studies have also shown that thoughts are part of a gene's environment and can affect its expression. People who were "cured" by taking a placebo in random clinical trials are dramatic proof of the important role that thoughts have in resolving health issues. We are told that eating well and regular exercise not only improves our quality of life but is good preventative health care. I believe it is as important to know thyself for the very same reason.

When Pat set her sights on a goal, she was a force to be reckoned with. The flip side to this determination is she can be equally stubborn. She was very capable of taking a stupid position on an issue and dig her heels where no one could budge her from that train of thought. She could be as non-compliant as some of the patients that she used to complain about. Doctors have a reputation of being uncooperative when they become patients themselves. People have a tendency to believe what they want to believe regardless of science or fact. This is also true for doctors. I am reminded by one of the songs by The Doors, "People are Strange". People can get real strange when it comes to medicine. However, a virtue like determination morphing into stubbornness was the least of Pat's problems. She had a deeper problem going on. The elephant in the room was a free-floating pathological fear of death that she had had from a very early age. I knew it was there and I thought it stemmed from taking care of her mother while she was dying of breast cancer. Pat and her father took care of her mother at home until she passed away. She told me about this years ago, but it was only now that she told me when her mother died it was from a second bout of breast cancer. Her first brush with breast cancer happened when Pat was very young. When her mother was hospitalized the first time, Pat was also in the hospital for an infection. Although they were just down the hall from each other she wasn't allowed to see her mother because of the infection. Pat remembered being really scared. While Pat was recounting this story to me, it was obvious she was reliving a traumatic event in her life. I think it was reasonable to conclude that this underlying fear of death was from this experience. Whether I am correct or not, this fear of death was like adding jet fuel to the anxieties and worries she had about her health. It clouded her judgment in decision making and the acceptance of possible treatments. It also neutralized her self-reliance, which had always served her so well in the past. Whatever its source, it should have been dealt with long ago, but for now it was part of the reality we had to deal with it. I was going to try and do my best to be a clear-headed counterweight to this irrational fear. Once I realized that Pat had this monkey on her shoulder, it helped explain some of Pat's challenging behaviours that came up from time to time. Anxiety attacks were actually fear attacks. If I had a hard time reading what was going on and I knew her best, it would be impossible for anybody else to understand what was going on with her. If this all sounds confusing, it was and made my job very difficult.

Our primary target for a new home was in the United States. We had a couple of options to gain legal status, but until such time we needed to have a Canadian home base. Halifax was the logical choice because Pat's liver surgeon was located there and Pat's youngest daughter lived there. Pat had attended medical school in Halifax and, despite having never liked the city, I convinced her to give it a fresh look. Besides, Canadians can spend up to six months in the US legally and we would only be spending half our time in Halifax at best considering we wanted to do other travelling in addition to exploring

US destinations. Our US base was going to be Philadelphia where my daughter lived, and the airline she worked for had a direct flight between the two cities. We could use the flight benefit to commute back and forth. Perfect. I got the car registered with Nova Scotia tags and got our NS health cards. Next we found Pat a primary care doctor to keep the six-month intervals of liver imaging and blood tests for her iron levels in place. I had assumed that we could use Pat's daughter's address for our Canadian presence. I was wrong. I guess in my rush to complete the move I missed signs that my assumption was incorrect. We ended up renting a nice loft apartment near the Armdale Circle. It was only August and I thought we might as well stay in Halifax for a while and travel south when it started to get colder. We spent most of our time at a relaxed pace trying to unwind from the last few years. We would take many walks along the several nice oceanside parks. It was only looking back now that I realized I was just as burned out as Pat was. Halifax is the biggest city in Atlantic Canada with several universities and is very cultural. Greater Halifax has a population of about three hundred thousand, but it didn't long take before I knew in my heart that Halifax wasn't a good fit for us. The winters are cold and wet with lots of cloud cover. In my opinion the cost of living and real estate prices were far higher than the place was worth. Finding a new Canadian base would have to wait. Halifax was a dead end and later in the fall we left for Philadelphia, which is where we wanted to be anyway. Philadelphia was going to be our base of operations until we settled on where our new home would eventually be.

THE HONEY MOON

Everyone has baggage and burdens but that's not who you are,
baggage and burdens are just add-ons, don't let it define you.

The first couple of months in Philadelphia were like a honey moon. At least that's how my daughter and her husband described us. In Halifax, Pat had been unsettled and the strain of life in the past couple years was not lifting. We liked Philadelphia and distancing ourselves from our troubles back in Atlantic Canada gave us a little psychological lift. We were only now starting to realize how much of a pressure cooker Pat's practice had become. We were also realizing the strain that we had been under. It was going to take time to unpack all of that. Pat like most doctors hated on-call duty and she happened to find her pager in one of her bags. She used to call the pager the "grim beeper". It was a symbolic moment when she threw that away and it gave her a sense of freedom. For three years after the sale of our home, I kept having a recurring dream that the new owners were on their way to take possession of the house and we hadn't moved out yet! The dream had a few variations: we hadn't moved our possessions out yet or the renovations were incomplete. Interestingly, I was never in a panic in the dreams. It felt more like frustration because the moving was somehow being stalled and was out of my control. I wasn't having panic attacks during my waking hours and was functioning normally, but looking back I think the dreams were a stress reaction.

For the first few weeks, we had no agendas or schedules. On previous trips, we had found our favourite coffee shops and restaurants and mornings usually started with a nice walk to a coffee shop or sometimes we would go for breakfast at Ida Mae's. My daughter's house was a couple of blocks from the metro, providing us with easy access to downtown Philly. Pat's beautiful smiles were returning and she was looking much better. My daughter and her husband were both flight attendants and were away much of the time, so we had the place to ourselves. My daughter and her friends provided us with a social life. This was also a breath of fresh air because for the past few years we had been living in virtual isolation. Some of her friends had a sidewalk music jam every Tuesday evening during the warm months and I joined in. Many of her friends were also in the process of renovating their homes. There were regular renovation parties where everyone would band together to help each other move their projects along. A few hours of work would be followed by several hours of socializing, which usually included food. There were many pot luck barbecues and brunches. It was fun and the stress of the last couple of years was melting away faster and more effectively than any pill could deliver.

There were some interesting characters in the neighbourhood. One pleasant evening my daughter's husband took me for a walk to show me more of the neighbourhood. We came upon a guy he knew who was barbecuing his dinner in the roll-up garage door of his warehouse. The door was right on the sidewalk so we stopped and chatted. He refurbished vintage cars for a living. After a few minutes, he invited us upstairs to show us something. When we topped the stairs we were in a fifteen-hundred-square-foot loft completely filled with model trains. He had a couple of different topographical set ups of model trains. Very detailed urban areas complete with homes and businesses. Another set-up was a mountain scene. There were also shelves of model trains behind glass. He had been collecting for decades and estimated he had $350,000 tied up in the collection.

Now that he was close to retirement he was planning on selling it off bit by bit to supplement his retirement income. Some of it was very collectible and would fetch a high price. I thought this was an innovative way to finance a retirement. Cash transactions that didn't require collapsing a retirement portfolio that could be subject to taxes.

The entrepreneurial spirit was alive and well in the neighbourhood and I found that exciting. Many people had limited or no access to bank loans and had to be creative in financing their projects. One of my daughter's friends bought an empty warehouse across the street from her house. He bought the building by selling another warehouse he had on Frankford Ave near Girard Ave. The first warehouse was abandoned and derelict when he bought it and, although he didn't have to do anything to it, its value rose substantially as gentrification spilled over into that neighbourhood. The ware house he bought was around 10,000 square feet. The building housed his bread and butter business, which was making replica steering wheels for 1964 and 1/2 to 1967 Ford Mustangs. The first tenant to rent space from him was a guy restoring vintage Vespa motor scooters. The rest of the building was stuffed with all manner of objects that he accumulated at yard sales, flea markets and estate sales. I thought he might be a serial hoarder until I found there was a plan behind this. He was buying and selling on a cash basis, avoiding a lot of taxes and other expenses, and was essentially building a nest egg like the guy with the model trains. He was reluctant in parting with any of acquisitions unless he really needed money. One such sale was a late Fifties VW van, which was rare enough, but this one was even more rare with sliding doors on each side. He got offers very quickly that shot up into the tens of thousands of dollars from as far away as Germany. There were many creatives living in the neighbourhood along with the entrepreneurs. One business that opened to serve the artisan market was the Sculpture Gym. They had a full array of wood working and metal fabrication equipment and rental space for artisans giving them full access to the shop equipment. I really liked the entrepreneurial/ artistic activity in the neighbourhood.

Art galleries across Philadelphia would hold open houses on the first Friday of each month. The First Fridays event was a fun carnival atmosphere. Some of the galleries had live entertainment and/or a buffet table of finger foods. In some areas the streets were closed off to vehicle traffic, allowing for street vendors. One of the businesses that participated in Fishtown was a shop that refurbished motorcycles. The shop was stuffed with motorcycles in various stages of repair and there were parts everywhere. The owner also picked up a mini helicopter that he had hanging from the rafters and he intended to restore at some point. On First Fridays he had blues band blasting away in the middle of the shop floor. The event filled the local restaurants and coffee shops. There was a pizza place in my daughter's neighbourhood called Pizza Brain. They served regular pizzas, but also other themed pizzas with topping, not normally found. They boasted of having the largest pizza paraphernalia collection in the world and the pizzeria served as a pizza museum. Frankford Hall was a brewery/ beer garden that brewed beer in the traditional German way. It was a good example of reclaiming an old industrial building. The back half of the building's roof had collapsed so it was just opened up and made into an open-air area with fire pits and a concession on each side so patrons could just walk up and order regular pub food.

Like all honey moons it was time for this one to end. We needed to start thinking what our next step should be. The fact that our future was like a blank slate was exciting to me. This was a moment to reinvent our lives and I saw this as a priceless opportunity. The respite did us both a lot of good and Pat was visibly feeling better. My daughter's home was a fixer upper when they had bought it and since they travelled so much the renovations had been delayed. They were gracious enough to put us up in their home so I offered to help with the renovations. After all, families help each other out. I had a lot of experience in renovations and if I knew what needed to be done I could continue the work if their jobs took them out of town. Pat really enjoyed helping and watching the progress of renovations and was looking forward to the project too. My daughter and her husband had two income properties. One was rented, but the other one needed renovations before it could be put on the rental market, so that project could be tackled next. They floated the idea that we could partner with them in rental properties. After the 2008 financial meltdown, I was willing to consider it as an option for generating a passive income stream now that the interest rates had collapsed. I had never invested in real estate before and wasn't sure if I wanted to deal with being a landlord.

A tried and true strategy for several generations was to invest in growth in the younger working years and migrating over to income-producing investments as you got older, approaching retirement. This was turned up side down in 2008 with the collapse of the interest-bearing accounts. In 2012, I went to the Bank of Canada and used their inflation calculator. Pat and I had known each for twenty years at the point. The Canadian dollar during those twenty years had lost 44.76 percent of its purchasing power. I was stunned! This was based upon a 1.87 percent inflation rate. Our retirement portfolio had been managed by one of the big bank brokerage houses and I decided to review our portfolio and the strategy they were using. They were taking the traditional approach and they were moving from equity investments into Canadian bonds that were now maturing at a less than a 2 percent yield. This was unacceptable; we couldn't live on that. To put this into another perspective, I applied the rule of 72. Take the interest rate you're getting and divide it into the number 72 and the result is roughly how many years it would take to double your investment. A 2 percent interest rate would take 36 years to double your investment. As I write this in 2019, the Bank of Canada's inflation calculator showed the dollar had now lost 62.26 percent based on a 1.81% inflation rate. Passively handing off the management of our retirement was more of a risk than I was willing to take. Our nest egg wasn't big enough to rely on and it needed to generate an income for us to be secure. It was for this reason I was willing to consider investing in income properties. I was really more interested in buying and flipping to build up our retirement nest egg rather than having income properties.

I am an observer. I tend to make decisions slowly and many times too slowly. I gather as much information as I can, but my intuitive sense has to be satisfied as well. My daughter's home was on the fringes of an old Irish neighbourhood called Fishtown, which was embedded in the greater area known as Kensington. The development in the neighbourhood was actually a spillover from the development that had already taken place in the Northern Liberties. The dividing line between the two neighbourhoods was East Girard Avenue. Even though all you had to do was cross the street, it still takes some brave souls to go into a rough and tumble area to get the ball rolling. These early adopters were called pioneers. By the time my daughter moved to the area, the "pioneers" had already blazed the trail and most of the drugs and criminal elements had moved out. Development was now moving quickly, but there was still a lot of opportunities. There were many older homes available for renovation or they could be demolished to make way for new construction. Mixed in with the detached homes and duplexes were some industrial buildings that were being converted to loft apartments or condos. I also liked the racial and socio economic mix in the neighbourhood. My daughter's home was one block from the metro blue line, providing easy access for people who worked downtown. This convenience was drawing young professionals to the neighbourhood. Two doors from my daughter's house was a young couple who were both physicians.

Pat and I were sitting on the back patio enjoying a late summer evening. In the middle of casual conversation, Pat said she was so angry when she was forced to take the MoCA test that she didn't read most of the questions and just chose random answers. After being momentarily taken aback, I got really pissed. You're telling me this now? You couldn't go along with the ridiculous test to keep your billing number? After I simmered down, I started thinking about what she said. This was classic Patricia behaviour. I knew Pat well and shouldn't have been surprised that she had done this. She was being forced to take the test and saw this as another layer of injustice piled onto the years of harassment that she had already been subjected to. I agreed with her that what happened was an injustice and my initial reaction of anger changed to understanding why she did it. The reality was, if she had refused to take the test, they would have found another reason to rescind her hospital privileges and take her billing number anyway. She was damned if she did and damned if she didn't. It was also classic for Pat to think things through for herself without consulting anybody. Once in a while she would blurt out something like this and I would find out after the fact. It wasn't that she was being deliberately secretive, but it was one of the confounding aspects of her personality.

Reviewing over and over again test results, image summaries, etc. is something I would do many times over the next few years. When Pat told me she sabotaged the MoCA test, I needed to revisit my conclusions about MoCA just to make sure my previous opinion was correct. I know I've covered this ground previously, but at the outset of this book my stated goal was to inspire people to get involved in their own medical care and learn about medicine. In that light, I hope this review serves as a useful example for processing information and the importance of leaving no stone unturned. I was expected to believe that the anxiety Pat had in writing the test would not affect the outcome. This implies that the test design is able to filter out the anxiety a patient, any patient, may have in being tested for a cognitive decline. Anyone who is knowingly being tested for cognitive decline is going to be nervous about the outcome and nervousness can affect performance. In addition to this, anxiety can be symptomatic for Alzheimer's disease and now the logic becomes circular. Somehow a test was magically designed to factor out anxiety and anxiety can be a part of the disease they are testing for. Now more specific to Pat's revelation, did the test design factor in that a patient could sabotage the test because they were angry for being forced to write it? Or is the patient who may not be of "sound mind" be expected to answer the questions honestly? If this all sounds like I'm going around in circles it's because I am trying to follow if this test was logically and thoughtfully designed. I have a degree in designing tests. It is not possible for a medical community to design a test to definitively diagnose Alzheimer's disease when they by their own admission know very little about the disease and can't say for sure if anyone has it. This simply does not make any sense.

What a mess! I'd like to have a nickel for every time this thought ran through my mind in the next few years. We didn't know it at the time, but really serious trouble was still ahead of us. I wanted Pat out of the practice, but I still wanted her to have to option to do medicine in some other capacity at a future date. The options for medicine were taken off the table now that she was labelled with AD despite the fact that the diagnosis was overturned. A more graceful dignified departure would have been preferable, but it was all water under the bridge now as far as I was concerned. Pat's career was important, but the hospital drama was a side show for my main concern, which was getting to the bottom of Pat's unanswered health issues. The biggest clue I had that there may a problem was Pat still lamenting a few years ago that there was something wrong with her brain. This was a mess alright and we would find out over the next few years just how much of a mess it really was.

Pat maybe should have taken the advice of the emergency room doctor earlier on and just walked away. Over the past several years there had been an increasing encroachment in physicians' private medical practices and some veteran doctors were leaving the profession because of it. The expectation to conform to standards of care and patient profiling was replacing the traditional doctor/patient relationship. Some held the view that quality of care was suffering as a result. Many also held the opinion that medical peer reviewing wasn't contributing to improving patient care and the true motivation was to force doctors to adhere to the desired protocols. The hospital decided to get in on the act by requiring doctors to provide access to their patient's medical charts to their respective department heads. The stated reason was monitoring quality assurance. The head of family medicine was a rookie salaried doctor who saw maybe eight patients on heavy day. Older doctors who saw forty-five to sixty patients a day thought her "oversight" was unnecessary. Besides, the hospital was in serious need of their own oversight. Many of the hospital's staff knew about the skeletons that the hospital had in its own closet. The hospital needed to look after its own affairs and mind their own business.

Our first choice was to live in the American south-west, but going further south to central America or the Caribbean was a possibility for the lower cost of living. We were concerned about being able to afford retirement and we spent some time online researching the pensionado programs of countries that were potential candidates. The flight benefits provided through my daughter's employment made it affordable to travel to the destinations that interested us and check things out first hand. We had already travelled to Mexico, Costa Rica, Bermuda and the Bahamas, our first excursion would be to the Dominican Republic for a couple of reasons. Their pensionado program was competitive and it was on the second biggest island in the Caribbean. Although it shared its land mass with Haiti, the DR portion was about the size of mainland Nova Scotia. Small islands were alright for vacations, but too small for our liking. The DR also goes up to about eleven thousand feet, offering several different climatic zones to choose from. We booked a bed and breakfast in the small northern town of Cabrera for a month. It was owned and operated by a couple of expat Floridians who also had a sport fishing business. Spending a month in the DR would help us log some time out of the US so we wouldn't overstay the six-month restriction. A month also would give us some time to look around and get a feel for the place.

We landed in Punta Cana and rented a car for the five-hour drive to Cabrera. The divided highway from Punta Cana west to Santo Domingo was brand new and was a beautiful drive. Just east of Santo Domingo we turned north onto another brand-new highway. Our hosts were very helpful in providing information about living there. They had lived in Costa Rica for seven years and their opinion was that DR was less corrupt and the infrastructure was far better. They were originally from the Florida Keys and had experienced hurricanes before and they chose Cabrera because it hadn't been hit by a hurricane for seventy years. Sounds good. Also Cabrera had a cliff shoreline and no beach front, which meant that it would never be developed for tourism. We had met several other of expat Americans and Canadians who were gracious in sharing their experiences living there. We were concerned about living in isolation because we didn't speak Spanish, but the expat was large enough to put that concern to rest. It was on this trip that I realized that, although I enjoyed the places that we had travelled to, I preferred the diversity of North America.

When we got back stateside, we started looking into getting legal status to live in the US. Pat had native American status from her previous marriage and we thought that might be a route to gain her green card. The Jay Treaty had been signed by the US and Great Britain in 1794 allowing First Nation North Americans the ability to travel freely across the border. Unfortunately this wasn't going to work for Pat because she had status by marriage, not by blood. This was a disappointment because if it had worked she could have then sponsored me as well. My daughter came with us to US immigration and when we returned to her house we were all sitting around on the sofa pondering what we could do next. I noticed my daughter was quiet and looked to be deep in thought. She then she took me by surprise by offering to upgrade from being a green card holder to becoming a US citizen. She then could sponsor me, then I would be able to sponsor Pat. I appreciated the offer and asked if she was sure she wanted to take that step. She said of course she wanted Pat and me to be able to move to the US. She liked the idea of being closer to family and she had no intention in moving back to Canada anyway. I called up Pat's cousin because she and her husband had already taken up US citizenship years ago. I wanted to know if there was any downside when they became US citizens. She said there were no drawbacks in doing so. She was still able to retain her Canadian citizenship and could hold both a Canadian and US passport, which had been useful on a couple of occasions. I just wanted to make sure that it wouldn't cause my daughter any problems. This was encouraging. It sure would solve the six-month limitation that we had to adhere to. Great! It was decided. Unfortunately, an unexpected turn of events would derail our plans to relocate to the US.

In between the Dominican Republic and Portugal trips we had an event. Pat had mentioned a couple of times that she was becoming too dependent on me. She was complaining about herself rather than trying to blame me for anything. Pat liked to go for walks around the neighbourhood and I would go with her, but she started asserting that she wanted to go for a walk by herself. My concern was her sense of direction, she didn't have a sense of direction. I understood that she didn't want to be held by the hand all the time. At first I secretly followed her because I didn't want her to get lost. In addition to a bad sense of direction: the neighbourhood was a bit of maze. Her walks were always the same routes that we walked together and were always in daylight hours. My daughter's house was one block away from Kensington's iconic milk bottle. This was actually a water tower on top of an old industrial building in the shape of a milk bottle. Philadelphia Historical Commission added the 120-year-old structure to the local historic register. When Pat told me that she was using it as a visual landmark to make her way back to the house it gave me added assurance that she would be alright. Then one day Pat was out longer than usual and I was starting to get worried. I jumped into the car and started driving around, but I couldn't find her. I started to get really worried when the sun went down. The fall evenings were getting cool and she wasn't wearing a coat. My daughter and one of her friends started making phone calls to police and hospitals. Five hours went by and, while my daughter's friend was driving me around the neighbourhood, her cell phone rang. It was the police and one of their members had taken Pat to a hospital a few blocks away earlier in the day. It's not clear why she had been approached by police, but when they asked where she lived she couldn't remember my daughter's address. She was also acting jumpy being approached by the police so they took her to a hospital.

We went to the hospital immediately. They had Pat in the psychiatric lockdown ward! The police for her "safety" had brought her to the hospital handcuffed in the back seat of the police car. The seats were hard, there were no door handles and she arrived at the hospital very frightened. When I finally got to see her she was very scared and crying, but otherwise safe and sound. At the emergency room she was able to provide her name and that she was a physician herself. The attending neurologist asked me basic questions confirming her name and any medications that she may be taking. I was very skeptical of neurologists by now, so I thought I would just listen to what the neurologist had to say. She told me that she suspected Pat had a cognitive issue and that she would usually attribute her behaviour to some form of dementia, but she said that something else was going on with her. I duly noted that! Now that we had arrived, she was discharging Pat so we could take her home. I was in a rush to get Pat out of the hospital and I regretted not asking the neurologist questions about what she thought the problem might be. Looking back on it, this neurologist was very sharp to rule out dementia or Alzheimer's disease after a brief investigation. A week later we got copies of Pat's emergency room chart along with copies of brain imaging on disk. The brain imaging was important to me because I never forgot the original neurologists in Halifax saying that, if Pat had Alzheimer's disease, her brain would further atrophy and more lesions would appear. The imaging done at the emergency room was three years after the first Spec CT and it showed Pat's brain virtually unchanged. I took this as good news. The next day Pat asked me a very important question that nearly crushed me. She said, "Are you going to throw me away?" I assured her that wasn't happening and she meant more to me than the breath of life itself.

Nearing the end of October 2014 we were on the road again to log some more time out of the US. One of Pat's doctor colleagues told us about a surgeon who was treating his patients with an innovative technology he had developed. His technology allowed him to treat and resolve conditions non-surgically. I was skeptical about alternative medicine and our doctor friend who was suggesting using the equipment for Pat's liver was on the eccentric side, which wasn't helping my skepticism. However, he had bought the equipment and set up a clinic and before we left Atlantic Canada I went to him to have my shoulder treated. The rotator cuff in my right shoulder and my right elbow was causing so much pain that it was difficult to raise a glass of water. After three hours of treatment, my elbow pain was gone and it has never returned and the treatment greatly improved my rotator cuff. Pat had only two out of her 2500 patients that she prescribed narcotics. One was for managing rotator cuff pain, so improving my shoulder was significant. His equipment wasn't designed for pain management, but to do actual tissue and bone repair. I thought why not go to the doctor that actually developed the equipment to have Pat treated? We called and made an appointment to see him. This appointment turned out to be very, very interesting.

ANSWERS THE HARD WAY
PART I

Peace of mind is worth a lot of money
My dad

We needed to log some time out of the US again, so we decided to drive to Lloydminster, Alberta, for the doctor's appointment we made for Pat. Then we would head back to Halifax through Canada. This was a total distance of 7500 miles or 10,500 kilometres. That's a lot of driving. Keeping track and making sure we didn't go beyond the six-month limit in the US was getting to be a real nuisance. We got on I-76 in Philadelphia and started heading west. Travelling through the US compared to Canada is a breeze. Gas, food and lodging are cheaper and the higher population density means that your never far from amenities. In Canada there are regions where it can be a long way to the next town, so when you come to a gas station you'd better stop to gas up and take your bathroom break. There are more twinned highways in the US, making for safer driving not having to deal with oncoming traffic. There many stretches on the interstates where the speed limit is 75 mph, enabling you to cover a lot of ground in a day. Then there is signage. We got lost twice, once near Lancaster, PA, and in Chicago but with ample signage we were able to get back on track within minutes. The Canadian highway system has poor signage even in urban areas and it's easy to end up on the wrong route. We stayed on the interstate highway system as far as North Dakota, where we turned north to go into Canada. It had been years since I had driven across North America and I completely miscalculated the time to get to our destination. I didn't want to be rushed and wanted to have time to make stops along the way if we saw something that interested us making the trip more enjoyable. My miscalculation turned our last day of driving into a marathon to get to the bed and breakfast we had booked.

We arrived for our 10am appointment the next morning and was met by the good doctor's wife and she ushered us into the waiting room. The mid-morning appointment allowed us a much-needed sleep in to recover from the hard driving from the day before. The clinic was attached to his home, with a spacious waiting room dividing their living quarters from the treatment area. Just the two of them operated the clinic with no additional staff. The doctor was taking a break after treating the previous patient and, while we waited, we chatted with his wife before he joined us. She asked about our mutual friend back east, the doctor who had originally treated me using this technology. When the doctor entered the room we continued the small talk, but he turned the conversation towards Pat's medical career. Pat explained she had been recruited by the Canadian military while she was in medical school and served a few years after graduation. When she was discharged, she went into private practice with an emphasis on obstetrics. She wanted to experience as much medicine as she could so she also did emergency room shifts, surgical assists and other aspects of medicine. She also talked about the dirty hospital politics at the end of her career and the difficulty of dealing with that. The toxic environment didn't surprise him because he'd had his own share of it over his career. He developed a technology that resolved medical issues without surgery and the associated risks, but mainstream medicine wasn't interested in his technology, so he left the system.

His medical career was very interesting. Most of his career was as a surgeon in the Belgian military. He came from a family of medicine: his mother was also a physician and his grandmother was a self-taught herbalist. This probably helped explain his interest in medicine from eastern cultures. He was well versed in ayurvedic medicine and acupuncture. His mentor whom he consulted on behalf of his patients was Japanese. He was part of the investigating team for the 1986 Chernobyl nuclear disaster. The most interesting part of his story was that he had been rendered paralyzed from the waist down due to a bomb blast while serving in Africa in the 1980s. It was his mother who found a rudimentary version of the equipment that he now uses with his patients. Using this equipment, he was able to restore his ability to walk without surgery. With this success, he reverse engineered the equipment and spent several years refining the technology. He was acquiring some of the electronic components through his former military contacts and as a result was contacted by CSIS (Canadian Security Intelligence Service), the Canadian equivalent of the US CIA. The electronic components were military grade and they wanted to know what he was using them for. Once he explained and demonstrated the equipment they were satisfied.

One item we didn't leave in storage was Pat's medical chart and we brought it with us just in case he wanted to review it. He asked what our medical concerns were and we told him the big issue was cirrhotic liver damage probably as a result from hemochromatosis. He asked what was being done for her liver now. We explained that she was being followed by a liver transplant surgeon in Halifax and she was getting liver imaging every six months, alternating between MRIs and ultrasounds. She was also getting blood tests every three months to check her iron levels and if the levels were high a phlebotomy was ordered. The blood test included Alpha-Fetoprotein, which was a cancer marker. I'll never forget his casual response for what the liver transplant surgeon was doing: "He's doing a study." The tests were keeping Pat in the surgeon's queue in case her liver quit and she needed a transplant, but these test results were also adding to a statistical data base. Comments and revelations like this over the years were incrementally opening my eyes to just how mainstream medicine operated. One of her daughters thought it was a good thing that she being followed by a liver surgeon, but to what end? A liver transplant? It was always in the back of mind that can't something else be done than to just wait for a ticking time bomb to explode? This was the best liver doctor had to offer?

He handed us both a medical questionnaire to fill out. I hadn't even considered getting treatment for myself and he said, well, since you travelled all this way, why not? I thought, well, why not indeed. Pat was going to be treated first. When I had made the phone call for the appointment I mentioned that Pat was very fearful of her damaged liver and she was concerned that a complementary medical approach could expose her damaged liver to further at risk. This was uncharted territory for her. Just before taking Pat into his treatment room, he looked directly into Pat eyes and clearly stated that he wasn't going to hurt her. She appreciated hearing the reassurance and she felt more relaxed. She then went into the adjoining treatment room. She stripped down to her underwear and lay face down on the massage table he used. I was asked to come in as he did a visual exam. He pointed some curvature of the spine and several protruding vertebrae could be seen below her shoulder blades. He also noticed an enlarged right kidney. Once the visual assessment was done, I was asked to go back to the waiting room, where I continued chatting with his wife.

During the week he imparted a lot of medical knowledge, but not so much on the actual technology itself. He may have considered that proprietary since he had developed it. Through the course of conversation he told me his device uses five different technologies. The three that I knew specifically were infrared, ultrasound and fMRI. Infrared basically acts like a heat pad, dilating blood vessels, drawing more blood to an injured area. The increased blood flow aids in healing. Unlike a heating pad, infrared heats deep tissues not just surface areas. Ultrasound is more complicated and there are different opinions on its effectiveness. The idea has been around for a while and the way it's explained is the ultrasound waves create a resistance that speeds up tissue and bone repair similar to weightlifting increasing muscle mass. I went online to see what I could find out about the use of ultrasound in healing soft tissue and bone. I found a company that used low-intensity pulsed ultrasound (LIPUS) in conjunction with 3-D printed casts to accelerate bone growth. Like everything else in medicine, the use of LIPUS had mixed reviews. The National Center for Biotechnology Information had done some research on the effectiveness of LIPUS, but hadn't reached any conclusions. They did acknowledge that LIPUS was gaining in popularity.

The stimulators for his device could be placed directly on an injured area or they can be placed on the acupuncture meridian lines. Cross-referencing available science with anecdotal stories had become my standard approach in our due diligence. Pain management and treating nausea from chemotherapy with acupuncture are two areas that have wide acceptance in mainstream medicine. Pat often referred her patients to a private pain management clinic that incorporated acupuncture in its therapies. The clinic was owned by a medical doctor who had training in acupuncture and many of Pat's patients had successful outcomes for pain relief there. Pat's radiologist cousin who organized the liver biopsy for her a few years earlier had come down with pancreatic cancer (he unfortunately passed away). He received regular acupuncture treatments for the nausea he had from the chemotherapy. He had no idea how acupuncture worked, but said it was very effective in treating his nausea.

There are many studies for acupuncture done both in the east and west that are readily available to review. In the early 1960s, a North Korean physician using a proprietary staining technique was able to identify very fine thread-like structures that corresponded to the acupuncture meridian lines. Even though structures were confirmed by Japanese researchers in 1967, Dr. Bonghan's work gained little interest by researchers partly because he didn't reveal his formula for the staining technique that he used. However, researchers at the Seoul National University again confirmed the existence of the "Bonghan lines" in 2003. These researchers in addition to using a staining technique also used modern imaging technologies: CT scans, MRI, infrared imaging, LCD thermal photography and ultrasound to confirm the existence of this anatomical structure. Apparently these lines in addition to being very fine and almost invisible are buried in connective tissues and if you weren't looking for them you wouldn't see them. They are also found inside blood and lymphatic vessels and form networks that overlay internal organs, blending in very well.

Traditional acupuncture says that the meridian lines is a system for the flow of energy they call qi. Today's researchers seem to have come to a similar conclusion. They believe these channels transmit energy and information using electromagnetic energy in the form of biophotons. It has been characterized as a fibre-optic system for the human body. The idea that acupuncture channels conduct energy was also substantiated by Russian research published in 1991. Other research has measured the energy using EKG and MRI technology. I have also read that the electromagnetic activity distorts the ability for microscopes to peer inside to accurately observe and study these anatomical structures. What I found particularly interesting was that granules of DNA containing chromosomal material "travel" inside them. The packets of DNA were readily responsive to the staining technique, making them clearly distinguishable. When these cells were isolated and then induced to differentiate, they grew into cells of all three germ layers. My translation: these may be our body's natural source of adult stem cells and stem cells are the foundation that specialized cells develop from. This may explain how acupuncture is able to repair tissues, but this is just my layman's guess.

Traditional acupuncture practitioners believe that there is an emotional component that plays an important role in a person's health. Cellular biology research seems to have made a connection to this as well. It was thought that the "brain" of any cell was the nucleus, which contains DNA and chromosomes. However, the nucleus of a cell can be removed and the cell will continue to survive. The brain analogy doesn't hold up obviously because, if the human brain is removed, the person dies. So what actually determines cell survival and function? Research is now pointing to the outer membrane that encapsulates the cell as the most important component. The cell's membrane is the gateway that allows what gets in and what gets out. This is all chemistry and the interplay of electrical charges. Nutrients pass the cellular membrane and waste material is expelled through the membrane. Nature is fascinating and wonderful, isn't it? I never had any interest in biology until I took a college-level course that I needed for a credit. Each cell is an intricate little machine containing several organelles to maintain itself and produce other cells.

However, problems arise when a monkey wrench is thrown into the machine. Everyone knows, if they get exposed to toxins from our environment, their health can suffer. Low-level exposures can be insidious and hard to detect. A better example is acute exposures like a chemical spill where entire neighbourhoods have to be evacuated. When these toxins arrive at a cell's doorstep, they can cause havoc. The cell membrane is porous and when a nutrient arrives with its unique electrical charge it interacts with a cell's portal, allowing it to pass. Conversely, waste material with its unique electrical charge interacts with an exit portal, allowing for the waste material to exit. The monkey wrench happens when toxins arrive with their unique electrical charge interfering with normal cellular function. The toxins distort the entry and exit portals, allowing some toxins in polluting the cell's environment or disallowing cell waste material to exit, contaminating the cell. In either case, the electrical charges of toxins and waste material interact with the electrical charges of DNA and chromosomes, causing them to "express" differently than under normal healthy conditions. This is why it is not accurate to say we are genetically "hard wired". I am being very simplistic to illustrate cellular biology and if you're so inclined you can go into greater detail on your own. It's fascinating and intriguing reading.

Now here is the incredible thing. There is some indication that one of the environmental influences that affects genetic expression are thoughts! Is this a stretch? Is this voodoo junk science? Participants in random clinical trials who are "healed" from placebos would seem to indicate that this is not a stretch. I don't think it can be characterized as junk science, but it is probably under-researched science. Thoughts are, after all, chemical activity and the interplay of electrical charges in the brain. Mainstream medicine has separated the mind from body in its paradigm, which to me is a mistake. It is mistake because our human experience is a physical body and our minds. Our personality and our emotions play a huge role in our lives for better and sometimes for the worse. In our everyday lives we don't think of our thoughts and chemical/electrical activity, but they are and, to be real, they are much more than that. Our thoughts, attitudes and beliefs are not insignificant contributors to our well being and our physical health to be ignored. So get to know "who" you are and "mind" what you think.

All of this explanation is not to make a case for acupuncture, but is an example of us trying to do our best for due diligence in choosing a path for medical treatments. Personally, I find the hard sciences interesting and it was intellectually satisfying to look into all this. If mainstream medicine hadn't failed Pat, I would never have taken a deep dive like this. In the end, results sre the only thing that matters. I already had positive personal results from this technology back east to go on and now we were about to achieve more impressive results with this doctor.

After Pat came my turn. I went through the same routine, getting down to my underwear and lying face down on the table. He did a visual assessment of me and asked me if I had ever been in a car accident. I said no and then he asked if I had ever fallen off a roof. I immediately remembered my eleven-foot fall coming off the roof of our house during renovations. I had waited until mid-afternoon for the dew to evaporate on the metal roofing that day. Despite my precaution, when I climbed off the ladder I started sliding. I was sliding on my belly backwards and I tried to spread eagle to stop the slide, but it wasn't working. I rolled over and sat up and prepared to hit the ground. I thought I would drop and roll, but instead I hit the ground and folded into myself like an accordion. I didn't break anything, but I was really stiff getting out of bed every morning for several months after. The reason he asked was that my right leg appeared shorter than the left and was probably due to that fall. Interesting, not that I ever noticed. He asked me if I had any health issues or complaints. I told him that the treatments I received in Atlantic Canada resolved my tennis elbow, but my right shoulder was still giving me trouble. I couldn't raise my arm above my shoulder and a movement like reaching into the back seat of the car from the front caused a lot of pain.

He covered me head to toe with the stimulators targeting specific areas for my complaints and also along meridian lines for a general health tune up. The stimulators were plugged into a controlling panel and could be individually adjusted. The controlling panel looked similar to a mixing board that you would see in a recording studio. While these stimulators were doing their work, he sat on a stool at the head of the table and used a small portable version of the equipment with smaller handheld stimulators and worked on my neck and shoulders. I wish I had brought a recording device because all the while he treated me he shared a lot of his medical knowledge and I learned a lot. Pat was treated for two hours a day for five days and I was treated for two hours a day for three days. Also on the first day he started Pat on an herbal tablet called Liv.52. He said he regularly prescribed it for military personnel in the Belgian army for liver problems. It is a hepatoprotectant and a detoxifier for improving liver function.

We returned to the bed and breakfast on that first day totally exhausted. We lay down on the bed at 7pm and didn't wake up until 8am the next morning. The same thing happened at the end of the next day. I usually wake up at least once in the night for a bathroom run, but both nights I slept a deep dreamless sleep. The doctor said that the healing activated from this technology can continue for up to three days after treatment. I guess our bodies were in deep repair.

The next day was the same routine: Pat was treated first, followed by my treatment. Over the week the doctor's wife was good company while Pat was being treated. I also watched several health-related videos, which introduced me to the functional medicine approach. I have found in the last few years that doctors who question the medical system or leave it entirely had themselves gotten sick and found no resolution to their health issues within the system. So they, like we did, decided to look else where. This is what happened to one of the leading proponents for the functional medicine approach. He was experiencing an unexplained degradation of his cognitive ability. He suspected his problem may have stemmed from a lengthy stay in China when he was working there. He was tested for heavy metal toxicity. His intuition paid off and his test results showed he had toxic levels of mercury. He started a chelation program to get the mercury levels down and his cognitive abilities were restored. Chelators are chemical agents that bind to mercury and then filter through the kidneys and eliminate from the body through urine. For western mainstream medicine to even consider heavy metal toxicity contributing to mental decline is virtually unheard of. The functional medical approach investigates for the root cause of a health issue and instead of treating symptoms. The common sense to this approach is self evident to me. It is a holistic approach that considers each patient individually because patients can have similar symptoms for an entirely different set of reasons. Each patient also may have more than one cause for symptoms and each cause needs to be ferreted out and addressed to resolve the issues. Modern western medicine treats the human body as if it were a collection of component parts. Treating human component parts and ignoring the synergy of human biology is a very limited view of medicine and has great potential for harm. This thinking is starting to change, but mainstream medicine is in need of much more reform and it's not coming fast enough in my opinion.

At the end of Pat's treatment on the second day, the doctor asked me in to see if I noticed anything different about Pat. She was lying face down, but I didn't notice anything different. He pointed out that the hump in middle of her back yesterday was now completely gone. He was right and this was after only four hours of treatment. I thought that was impressive. On the third day he worked heavily on my right shoulder and from the shoulder up the right side of my neck with the handheld stimulators. The purpose was to repair any muscles that may have been compromised adjusting to the injured rotator cuff and to loosen up and make the muscles more supple. By the end of the week, not only could I raise my right arm above my shoulder, but I could do chin ups. The pain was gone and at the time of this writing it has been six years with no relapse of rotator cuff discomfort or pain and with no further treatments. On the last day of my treatment Pat came into the room and got spooked. The stimulators can be dialled up or down for intensity. The higher the setting the more work the device is doing and the faster healing is the result. The higher setting can cause muscles to contract and since I was covered head to toe my whole body had muscles contracting. I must have looked like someone having an epileptic seizure or convulsions. This upset Pat and she thought this might be causing me injury. Even though my body was shaking like that, I was still carrying on a normal conversation with the doctor. As the week progressed we were less tired at the end of the day. On the fifth and final day, I asked him if he thought the treatments had benefited Pat's liver. He flatly stated the cirrhotic tissue was gone. I was a little stunned and a lot skeptical. The general consensus in mainstream medicine is the damaged tissue from cirrhosis is permanent. I could plainly see with my own eyes earlier in the week that her back was straight. My right shoulder's mobility was restored and I was pain free for the first time in three years. I wasn't sure what to think about her liver. Pat was due for her semi-annual liver imaging and when we got back to Halifax we would make an appointment to have it done and the images should be able to confirm if this was true.

Pat's last session was on Friday and we started our 2500-mile journey back to Atlantic Canada the very next morning. I woke up early, packed up the car, had breakfast and in the back of my mind something was different, but couldn't put my finger on it. Once we got on the road I realized that my tinnitus was gone. Tinnitus is commonly described as a ringing in the ears, but there are several variations of this unwanted sound like humming, clicking, hissing and sometimes, as in my case, cricket sounds. Years ago I had mentioned to Pat that I heard "frequencies" and she said that had I tinnitus. I didn't know what that was and she explained to me that had hearing damage. I had been living with it for so long that I was accustomed to it and thought it was normal. I was surprised when she told me that it was a hearing impairment. Pat was able to get me an appointment with a neurologist and she examined me for possible causes. Ear wax captures dirt and fights bacterial growth, but too much build up can cause tinnitus. I didn't have too much ear wax so that was quickly ruled out. She noticed that both my ear drums had ruptured in the past. I said that was due to ear infections when I was younger and I told her I was still prone to ear infections. She said it was unusual for adults to have ear infections and thought that maybe there was a problem with the eustachian tubes. These are tubes that run from the middle ear to the back of throat and nose. The tubes help regulate ear pressure and drain excess fluid. She didn't order any imaging, but she was probably right because, when I get a cold, it can take weeks for the fluid to dissipate in my ear, reducing my hearing during that time. The neurologist said that there was nothing that could be done and I would have to learn to live with it. Yet after six hours of treatment here I was free from tinnitus for the first time in decades. Furthermore, I never even thought to mention it when I filled out the questionnaire. The doctor didn't know, interesting. The quiet in my head was refreshing.

At the same time I was realizing my tinnitus was gone, Pat was having a massive anxiety attack.

The entire 2500-mile trip was very difficult and it was touch and go if I would have to take her to an emergency room along the way. Both of us had just gotten very significant and promising results from these treatments and this was extremely discouraging. Our trip across Canada was a white-knuckle ride, but we made it to Halifax. Now that the long drive was behind us Pat was settling down a bit, but judging by the expression on her face she was clearly still distressed. The easing of her anxiety was to be short-lived. We hadn't been at her daughter's house for more than a few days when she asked us to leave. Now what do we do? She told us her husband was a very private guy and found it stressful for us to be there. Sure, no worries, we rented a hotel room for a few days while I scrambled trying to find a short-term rental. This put us in a difficult position. We made the trans-continental trip across Canada and I took it for granted that we would be able to stay at her daughter's house. I was so wrapped up in trying to deal with Pat's anxiety that I was probably blind to how it was affecting them. This development caused Pat's anxiety to spike again and it would continue to build for the rest of our time in Halifax. The hotel room was expensive, so I found a cheaper bed and breakfast for the time being until I could find us a place to stay.

The pressure was on, but I had to keep my cool. It had always been doubtful that Halifax was going to be a place where we would settle down. I gave it a half-hearted look, but it was now clear that it couldn't serve as a temporary safe harbour when we needed one. This presented a problem. We needed to spend six months a year in Canada to retain our Canadian Medicare and we couldn't stay more than six months in the US. This wasn't an immediate concern, but it would need to be resolved. For now Pat was due for her six-month liver imaging and we wanted to get this done to confirm that there was no more cirrhotic liver tissue after the treatments she received out west. If this was confirmed, it would be a very big deal. Getting an MRI appointment in Canada's single-payer government-run medical system can take months and for this reason we made an appointment at a private clinic and paid out of pocket. The results would also come back quickly. Pat still had boxes of her patient's medical charts and, since she was only required to keep her own clinical notes, we destroyed everything else. Copies of that paperwork could be gotten from the hospital if needed. Since Halifax wasn't going to be our Canadian address, we decided to move our belongings to a storage unit back in our home town where my grand daughter still lived. She was willing to help us if we needed things from storage and would help arrange shipping our things once we had found a place to live.

When we made the appointment for the liver MRI, I didn't give the radiologist a heads-up that Pat had liver disease or that her right kidney was slightly enlarged. I also held back that she had a liver biopsy showing that she had liver cirrhosis. His report noted the unusual shape of the liver and said that this was usually due to liver fibrosis. Since the liver tissue appeared homogeneous, lacking the coarse tissue that would be indicative of cirrhosis, he speculated that the deformity may be a birth defect. Although the tissue was homogeneous, he did note that it more looked more like muscle tissue which suggested mild iron disposition throughout the liver. He knew Pat had hemochromatosis and that was a reasonable conclusion to make. The duct appeared normal, but he did find one gall stone. The surgeon back in Alberta said that the gall stones were gone so this was a discrepancy. Her spleen and pancreas were normal and the right kidney showed no signs of hydronephrosis, urine retention. This was the most likely cause for the enlarged kidney that was observed out west, but now the kidney was normal. The liver had no lesions either.

I decided to call the radiologist and talk to him. The conversation basically reiterated his report with more detail. I was interested in his thoughts about Pat's odd-shaped liver. He mentioned that it could be a possible birth defect and added that the liver may have been subjected to some sort of trauma in the past. He couldn't say definitively. I stopped fishing and I came out and told him that she had had a biopsy done a couple of years ago and it showed that she had a cirrhotic liver. This surprised him. Damaged liver tissue is more coarse and can have lesions. The absence of lesions and the homogeneity of the liver tissue contradicted cirrhosis. This was interesting. Cirrhotic liver tissue is not known to revert to healthy tissue. I explained to him the treatments that we received the week before in Alberta and the MRI seemed to confirm that the treatments did indeed cause a reversal of cirrhotic tissue to healthy tissue. I also told him that my painful rotator cuff after a few hours of treatment was now pain free for the first time in years. The radiologist had rotator cuff pain and he was trying to manage it with physiotherapy and painkillers. He asked for the doctor's name and phone number in Alberta and I provided it to him. I don't know if he followed up.

Pat's anxiety progressively got worse all the while we were in Halifax. I was burning the candle on both ends between trying to settle her down and taking care of needed business. Everything came to a head one evening and there was nothing I could do. Out of desperation I took her to her daughter's house and we both tried to talk her down without success. It would be another year before I would find out a major key to the basis of this ongoing anxiety. Unexplained behaviour is difficult to deal with when you know that it is not in keeping with the person's personality. It's easy to just throw up your hands and yell at them to straighten up and act right. At a loss, I asked if she wanted to go to an emergency room and see if they could help. She agreed to this and her daughter came along. I don't why she agreed to go to the emergency room because when we got there she had a change of heart and totally lost it. I shouldn't have been surprised considering how the system had treated her over the last couple of years professionally and medically. It was a stupid judgment call on my part to have suggested it. She bolted like a scared animal. I caught up to her and tried to talk her down, but she was having none of it. Adjacent to the hospital was a big green common and I left her alone to let her walk it off. I joined her daughter, who was talking to hospital security to see if they could help us get her in to be seen. They explained that they had no authority to force someone into the emergency room and that patients have to walk in on their own. While we were talking things over, I looked back at the park and Pat was no where in sight. I did a quick march up an incline and couldn't see her anywhere. Now what should I do? Her daughter suggested calling the police and I went along with it. This was a decision I would soon regret.

The last few years had been difficult, but this was rock bottom for me and I felt I had just betrayed Pat. Her daughter tried to reassure me that I had not. She thought that the police would be able to force Pat into the hospital where the hospital security could not. From the start, I had been butting heads with everyone from the hospital to the family concerning Pat's health issues. I had clearly articulated doubts to everyone in the family about the medical care Pat had received and welcomed challenges to my conclusions because I could be wrong. What was important was to get to the bottom of Pat's health issues for the best possible treatment. Pat's daughter had suggested institutionalizing Pat from the very beginning, but I dismissed that out of hand. To me that was a cop out. Much of Pat's unexplained behaviour in the last few years was very difficult, but I was also at a loss with the behaviour of the family not wanting to help us out. Pat's anxiety spikes were out of character and should have been recognized as a symptom of an underlying issue. I wondered, if Pat had been diagnosed with liver cancer, would their reaction had been any different? Would the family have been more understanding and willing to stand by her? Or would they have walked away from the ravages of that disease and the hell of chemo-therapy that she would have to go through? In the end, actions speak louder than words and so far we had fought this battle on our own and going forward we would have to continue to fight it on our own.

When the police arrived, we explained the situation and gave them a description. In less than half an hour she was found about two blocks away walking in a residential neighbourhood. A police car came by and drove us to her. When we got in the police car the officer said don't be alarmed, but we have her in handcuffs. WHAT? Now I really felt like a piece of shit. The reasoning was that it was police procedure for her safety and theirs. I am not disputing that there are instances when someone needs to be placed in hand cuffs, but police training surely must include discretion. Placing a sixty-year-old woman unnecessarily in handcuffs was not beneficial to anyone. Pat's daughter called them and they knew that they weren't dealing with someone high on drugs. This was only going to exacerbate the crisis that Pat was experiencing. Pat was terrified being handcuffed and when I got there they immediately had them removed. After the handcuffs were removed, I put my arm around Pat and we walked away from the police and her daughter. What a mess! A week later we were back in Philadelphia.

ANSWERS THE HARD WAY
PART II

Finally...
the pace seems to be slowing
breathing is fast and shallow,
standing still now, panting,
blessed peace is returning.
The beast now tired, sleeps.
And like that, it dissipates
like a tornado in all it's fury, it simply
recedes into the night sky
leaving behind some territory
untouched and others decimated.
Tomorrow is another day

We were back in Philadelphia for three days and Pat went for a walk and didn't return. This happened once before and we found her in a couple of hours. This time she was missing for three horrifying, agonizing days. I was frantic. We called all the hospitals, we called the police, we canvassed the neighbourhood, we put up posters, but none of our efforts were producing results. Philadelphia was going through a July heat wave and I walked through empty lots searching the high grass in fear that she may have succumbed to the heat. I was desperate. This was terrible beyond words. We filed a missing person report and a detective was assigned to find her. He said I could call him any time and he also called me a couple of times to keep me posted. We did find one lady who lived at an apartment complex about four blocks away who recognized Pat from a photo we showed her. She said she was walking her dog and Pat stopped to pet him. This was also a half block from a dog park where Pat used to like to go sit to watch the dogs play. This was the only person we found that had seen Pat. My daughter and her friends mobilized social media and community blogs to spread the word. I didn't sleep much during those three days. Around two o'clock one morning I went to the police precinct where we had filed the report and couldn't get in because it was after hours. There was a police car parked on the street with an officer in it and his window was rolled down. I told him about Pat and was worried that the worst may have happened. He looked at me sincerely and he said he didn't think so and that she was out there somewhere. He told me to be patient and that she would be found at some point. On the second night I broke down and sobbed like a child. Then on the third day, we got a call from her daughter living in Toronto and she said she had found her. Even though we had called all the hospitals, she called them all again. They all told her that they had no Jane Does, but she was insistent and they checked again. Her insistence paid off. Hahnemann hospital told her they had a Jane Doe that had been admitted on the night that Pat went missing. The description she provided of Pat sounded similar to the patient they had admitted. My son-in-law and I rushed to the hospital and it was indeed Pat. She was found!

When we arrived at her room, Pat was in a wheelchair looking haggard and withdrawn. She didn't recognize me until I got right up into her face and only then did she realize who I was and she broke down and cried. The personal care worker that was assigned to her asked me if I knew her and I said she is my wife. She said this woman is a hot tamale. Chart notes from the emergency room described Pat as polite and cooperative. However, the next day she started to grow impatient and wanted to leave. Her impatience grew to defiance to the point where she was vaulting over the bed trying to get to the door to make a break for it. That's my girl. Her personal care worker was a wonderful young black woman standing at about six feet tall and Pat was even a handful for her to deal with. This is why she referred to her as a hot tamale. The reason Pat didn't recognize until I got up close was because she had been heavily sedated with benzodiazepines. It would be a couple of years later that I would learn that these drugs themselves can cause brain damage. This drugged-up condition gave me a glimpse at what her life would be like if she were ever placed in long-term care. Despite the diagnosis of Alzheimer's disease in 2010 being overturned, most of the family still thought it might be best if Pat were put in a home. Best for whom? They also were fully aware that the AD diagnosis was politically driven by the hospital. What needed to be done was to get a correct diagnosis and see if a proper treatment could resolve her symptoms. To have her placed in a home was an extremely premature decision to make. Pat is a "hot tamale" and long-term care certainly would have used drugs to manage her just like they were doing here in this hospital. We have some very sharp people in the family and I tried to recruit their collective talents to help find a solution, but it was to no avail. We were alone in trying to get to the bottom of Pat's health issues and this was now going into its fourth year.

It wasn't long after our arrival that the attending nurse came to see me. She explained that, on the night of Pat's disappearance, the police had observed her wandering the streets in the early morning for several hours before they stopped to see if she was in trouble. She seemed confused so they brought her to Hahnemann's emergency room at 2:47am on July 2, 2014. The neighbourhood they found her in was many blocks away from my daughter's house. Pat really got lost this time. She didn't know my daughter's address, so the police felt they had no alternative but to take her to an emergency room. First impressions in the emergency room were that she was in no apparent distress. She was comfortable and was being cooperative. Her behaviour was appropriate for her age and she'd denied that she was in pain and denied she was an abuse victim. When asked her name she couldn't/wouldn't provide it. It wasn't until the following year in 2015 that I would find a significant possible clue as to why Pat didn't provide her name. For now it was inexplicable to everyone including me why she didn't provide her name. Since they had no health history, several tests were started in the emergency room. A sepsis screen was ordered to see if she had any infections and they returned negative. A nutritional test showed no deficits. A urine sample was taken to test for alcohol and street drugs. They even tested her for West Nile Virus. A neurological exam was given. Pat was alert and keenly responsive and was able to follow commands and name objects. However, she was unable to form any new memories or repeat the names of objects on immediate recall. An abdominal image saw the abnormal shape of her liver so they did a liver function test. An under-functioning liver can cause ammonia build-up, which can cause cognitive disorders. Her ammonia levels were fine. Her comprehension seemed fine, but she had difficulty speaking (expressive aphasia) so their suspicions turned toward a possible stroke or a seizure. At 4:47am the decision was made to have her admitted. Pat was aware of the decision and at 5:44 she was taken to the floor.

Four years ago Pat's career was ended by a bogus political diagnosis. Her real health concerns received negligible medical investigations to add insult to injury. Already the investigations done at Hahnemann's emergency room just in a few hours was far more thorough than anything done in Canada in the past four years! The first doctor I met not long after the attending nurse was an internal medicine doctor. I didn't know it at the time, but Hahnemann is a teaching hospital and each of the specialists that were investigating Pat had their own entourage of medical students in tow. The specialist started asking me questions and I asked if he wanted to see Pat's medical chart. He stopped and turned to me with a surprised look: not many patients he met could supply their own medical chart. I was now faced with a decision to take her home or let Hahnemann hospital continue investigations hoping that they would find real answers to her health problems. We were uninsured Canadians in Philadelphia, but I was willing to throw caution to the wind for what I saw as an opportunity. Pat wanted out and she hated my decision to keep her there.

The next day I met the neurologist leading the charge. He was one of the nation's preeminent doctors in his field. He burst into Pat's room with his entourage wearing a leather jacket and a Superman T-shirt. They say that the eyes are the window to a person's soul. His eyes had fire and passion in them. After introductions, he started asking me questions about Pat. This was the first doctor to talk to me in four years that wanted to hear what I had to say. Good doctoring includes interviewing family members to gain insight and information to help them take care of patients. He wasn't the only doctor: each of the specialists questioned me to glean information that might be useful to them. This was a different experience than I had back in Canada, where I wasn't consulted and I being accused of being in denial. Here I was shown consideration, kindness and respect. What a relief. The neurologist jotted down notes to my answers and once in a while would turn and talk to his medical students. When he was done he turned and looked me straight in the eye and said, "We're on this and we're going to find out what's going on." With that he shook my hand and left the room as quickly as he came in. That was a very emotional moment for me: finally maybe something could be done.

I was interested in seeing their brain imaging results. The first neurologists that we had seen in Halifax four years ago said that a characteristic of an Alzheimer's brain was severe atrophy and lesions. At that time Pat had slightly more atrophy in the prefrontal lobe for her age and I was curious to know if there had been any further progression of either of these two features. I talked to the neurologist and he reviewed the previous brain image summaries from Pat's chart and he couldn't say there was a significant increase in brain atrophy.

I took this as a good sign that the original Alzheimer's diagnosis was incorrect. However, this benchmark was going to be completely called into question by another neurologist in 2015.

These are some of the findings of the brain imaging that was done during this hospital stay. A CT of her head showed that the ventricles that contain the cerebrospinal fluid (CSF) were normal in size, shape and position. There was no evidence of extra-axial fluids including CSF or any sign of hemorrhaging. There was no acute territorial ischemia, which meant her brain was getting a good blood supply. The mid-line shift or mass effect means that the brain was in the position it should be so no undue pressure was applied to the brain. She had an MRI with a contrasting agent that exposed some abnormalities (I would find out four years later the controversy about the contrasting agents used for MRIs). Imaging results suggested a global disposition throughout Pat's brain that probably were iron deposits due to hemochromatosis iron overload. However, a Spec CT of the brain suggested that the deposits in the basal ganglia may be calcium deposits instead of iron. If so, Pat might have Fahr's Syndrome. This is a rare inherited neurological disorder characterized by abnormal deposits of calcium in areas of the brain seen primarily in the basal ganglia and in other areas such as the cerebral cortex. This disease has several symptoms including speech problems. The final discharge summary went with a global disposition of iron deposits throughout Pat's brain, probably due to hemochromatosis. This seemed to confirm my suspicions from years ago that Pat's brain may have iron overload. The final discharge summary was extrapyramidal dysfunction secondary to PANK2 mutation versus iron disposition secondary to hemochromatosis.

The discharge summary also stated that Pat's cognitive function had improved, but hadn't returned to base line. The only functional deficit that the occupational therapy assessment identified was the speech problem. Extrapyramidal dysfunction was offered as an explanation. Extrapyramidal is part of the autonomic nervous system that controls automatic functions like breathing. This might have also been the explanation for Pat's speech deficit. The iron deposits in her brain could also have been the source of her speech problems as well. The discharge summary also identified possible procedural dysfunction. Pat sometimes would have trouble with simple things like opening a car door or with zippers on clothing. She noticed she was having these problems and didn't understand why. After seven days of investigations by several specialists at a prestigious US teaching hospital at a cost of $250,000.00 there was no definitive answer.

There was a couple of follow-up appointments after Pat was discharged with one of the neurologist interns and I was eager to talk to him about the liver imaging. The liver imaging done at Hahnemann had virtually the same summary as the MRI summary that had been done in Halifax three weeks earlier. The liver tissue was homogeneous in appearance and the echo texture was consistent throughout. Again there was no indication of liver cirrhosis. I asked the neurologist directly if the imaging wasn't showing any cirrhotic liver tissue. He said it didn't seem to be. I explained to him the treatments that Pat had received in Alberta. This young neurologist was from India and was familiar with the kind of technology that the doctor in Alberta was using, but it wasn't being used in the US. He added that the liver biopsy that we had done previously was the gold standard and, to verify if the cirrhosis was gone, another biopsy would be required. I didn't want to put Pat through that again, particularly since she just endured a seven-day stay at the hospital. The subject then turned to Pat's brain. His opinion was the global disposition in Pat's brain was iron deposits, specifically in the basal ganglia, which could be the cause of Pat's speech impediment. In my mind I was thinking, "You just said that a liver biopsy was the gold standard to prove if Pat still had a cirrhotic liver." Then how could he know that the global disposition in Pat's brain was iron? Pat had hemochromatosis and iron would be a good guess, but it's still a guess. He also said that the iron in her brain could not be removed.

I wasn't so sure he was right. When Pat was getting phlebotomies to lower her iron, I read up on how that worked. Iron in the blood is stored in the hemoglobin so when you remove blood the body's response is to make new red blood cells. This in turn triggers the stored iron in tissues and organs to be released and transported to the bone marrow for the manufacture of new red blood cells. This repeated procedure gradually depletes the stores of excess iron and eventually the iron levels fall. So does this mechanism reduce iron stores in brain tissue? I was aware of the blood/brain barrier, but how could he say for sure that stored iron in the brain is not released? I started out being very impressed by the thoroughness of investigations done by Hahnemann hospital, but we were still only getting guesses and assumptions. Discrepancies in opinion and uncertainties of findings make it very difficult trying to apply due diligence in making medical decisions. Who do you trust?

In the beginning all I had was common sense and some science background, but now my knowledge base for medicine was increasing. If the neurologist was correct that iron deposits in Pat's brain was causing the problem with her speech and mild cognitive impairment, then an effective treatment for this was the answer. The only treatment they were offering was the use of brain medications. We had already had the unpleasant experience of Exelon landing Pat in the emergency room. I would come to know later how these drugs can exacerbate brain problems rather than cure a health issue. I still held the view that prescribing a drug that affects brain function is risky business for an organ medicine knows little about.

Astronomical spectroscopy claims that it can determine temperature, density, mass, distance, luminosity, relative motion and the chemical composition of stars that are light years away. Astronomy can determine all this information, but medical science can't determine what the foreign deposits in someone's brain is without doing an invasive biopsy? Was medical science that far behind astronomical science? If that technology doesn't exist, then why hasn't it been developed? Each element has its own spectral emission so there is an identifier between iron and calcium. Existing PET scan technology already has the ability to detect cancer cells because they have a higher metabolic rate than healthy cells. PET scanning of the brain uses tracers that bind to glucose to detect glucose activity in the brain. Contrasting agents are used by radiologists to help them "see" what's going on, but the technology to "see" the difference between iron and calcium doesn't exist? In addition to these questions, how is it that even with these sophisticated and expensive machines two radiologists can have opposite interpretations of the same images? This is a problem that we would run into many times. A certain degree of differing image interpretations can be expected, but when the interpretations are completely opposite of each other that is a serious problem. What is the explanation faulty equipment, substandard medical training or something else? This is why in time the only medical metric that meant anything to us was results. Nothing else matters.

At the second follow-up appointment, another neurologist was invited to take part. This turned out to be really interesting. When Pat was told that she had Alzheimer's disease, she did the same thing when she was told she had hemochromatosis. She researched the hell out of it. Researchers found Alzheimer's brains had a build-up of a protein called beta-amyloid plaques in between the synapses of the brain. The theory was that this was impeding synaptic function. The neurologist that was joining in on the follow up was one of the researchers that had discovered this. She perused the chart from Pat's seven-day hospital stay and interviewed Pat. She said Pat seemed to have a stuck drawer syndrome, meaning that the information was still in Pat's brain, but she was having trouble retrieving it. Before she left, she turned and looked Pat straight in the eye and said, "You don't have Alzheimer's disease so don't even think about it." WOW! So now we have an internationally recognized Alzheimer's researcher confirming what the internationally recognized psychologist had said a few years earlier. Neither of them believed that Pat had Alzheimer's disease. GREAT!…now what?

The seven-day stay at Hahnemann generated 201 pages of charts and a $250,000.00 bill. I put $7,000.00 on a credit card and when I got home I submitted the receipts to the Canadian medical system for reimbursement. I was reimbursed for what these services would have cost in Canada. I got a check for $273.00. The US medical system is seriously inflated, but inflated by $6727.00? The Hahnemann investigations were exponentially more thorough than anything she received in Canada so maybe the difference in cost can be partially explained by you get what you pay for. I maxed out my credit card, but this still left a $243,000.00 outstanding bill. I provided Hahnemann with our Canadian health care card number and the contact information for Health Nova Scotia. Hospital collections deal with insurance companies and they accepted my Canadian health insurance card as just another insurance company to collect from. I have no idea how it turned out, but I suspect they were only reimbursed for a fraction of the outstanding balance like we were. My daughter explained that in Philadelphia an outstanding medical bill does not affect your credit score or the ability to qualify for a mortgage. My cousin happened to be visiting from Massachusetts at the time and he said it was the same in his state. Furthermore, a speech therapist that Pat starting working with after being discharged from the hospital said this was also true for Arizona. She gave the example of an illegal being brought to the emergency room who had been injured on a construction site. He ended up with a year-long stay despite having no health insurance or any ability to pay the medical bill.

Hahnemann made arrangements for weekly visits at home for a speech therapist to help with Pat's speech impediment. Pat had also expressed interest in the past for counselling sessions. After a few phone calls I was able to find a counsellor that would try to work with Pat despite having speech problems. Since the treatments we received in Alberta were successful, I decided to buy a portable unit of this device so we could treat ourselves at home. My right shoulder rotator cuff was repaired out west and when my left shoulder started having the same problem I was able to treat it myself. One night when we were out for dinner, all of a sudden I had the sure signs of a retinal detachment in my right eye. Flashing light in the periphery of vision and so many floaters in my eye that in looked similar to a flock of birds all flying in one swirling group. I didn't realize at the time that this was considered a medical emergency that could result in a permanent loss of vision. The common treatment for retinal detachment is laser surgery. Laser treatments form scar tissue to repair the tear. I treated myself and the light flashes stopped in the first thirty minutes. I treated myself a few more times and most of the floaters dissipated. When I told a friend what happened, first he was surprised that I was able to treat myself. He underwent laser surgery to repair his retinal detachment.

I wanted to get back on track of rebuilding a future for ourselves. Before the hospital stay, we were considering investing in rental properties, but I was never sold on the idea. We found talking with some of my daughter's friends that there was a market for short-term rentals. This sounded more interesting to me. With short-term rentals, I could take a credit card to book the apartment and if damage should occur I could charge the repairs to the client's card. This way I could avoid the possibility of having bad tenants with long-term rentals. My daughter was also interested in short-term rentals for her properties. She and her husband were out of town much of the time and we could help manage their rentals while they were away. They could do the same for us when we were travelling.

When Pat went missing, the subsequent hospitalization was hard on the family. Pat's oldest daughter suggested having a family video conferences once a week to keep in touch. I welcomed the idea of having a virtual family get-together. I wanted Pat and her daughters to have more contact with each other. I told her daughters about the

Alzheimer's disease researcher assuring Pat that she didn't have AD. I thought this be encouraging for them and also hoped they would join in the effort to help solve Pat's health issues. They still had no interest in getting involved. The idea that Pat should be institutionalized and that I was in denial remained. Pat and I were always the subject of the conferences and it was difficult to restore some kind of normalcy when the family thought of us as abnormal. The family video conferencing wasn't working and I didn't see any point in continuing it.

The speech therapy lasted for several weeks, but Pat lost interest because she couldn't see how flash cards were going to be of much help. Frankly I couldn't see how they were going to be of much help either. To make matters worse, Pat was insisting on going for walks in the neighbourhood by herself again. We had some very intense show-downs with her over this. Neither my daughter nor I could understand why she was taking such an obstinate stand on walking alone. It would be another year before I would find out why she wanted to walk so much, but for now the situation was getting intolerable. This strain had reached a breaking point with my daughter and her husband. Looking back on this time I should have realized this was coming. I wanted for things to work so much that I was seeing things through rose-coloured glasses. Looking back I also realize that I was in a serious burn-out. Things came to breaking point with my daughter and we had no choice but to leave. Our goal for relocating to the US was now gone. This was a difficult for me to come to terms with. I didn't know what to do. There was only one place to turn to and that was my granddaughter. Without hesitation she told us we could come and stay with her until we got ourselves sorted out. The scary part was we were going to back to the community where all the troubles had started. We were going home.

BURNED OUT AND A REFUGEE

This scarring event has its own power.
In the midst of which I've learned how to cut myself some slack

We left Philadelphia in October 2014. Over the past year we had brought a lot of our belongings to Philly as we travelled to and from Canada. My granddaughter also shipped a lot of our belongings to Philly as well. We did this because we had no intention of moving back to Atlantic Canada and Philly was going to be the hub for our activities until we figured out where our permanent home was going to be. Now I had to pack everything up and bring it back to Canada. We bought a roof rack for the car to bring back what we could, but most of it had to be shipped. The drive north to Atlantic Canada was nine hours long. This gave me a lot of time to think. I was at a loss. I had no vision going forward and felt directionless. We had wanted to get out of Atlantic Canada for years and leave the troubles behind. When we were finally able to leave, it was like getting out of jail. Starting a new life was an adventure and I was excited about it. We were going to travel and, since we were staying with my daughter for the interim, I would get to spend some time with her. This was a time of some uncertainty, but it was also a time of great opportunity where we could reshape our lives into what we wanted. I wasn't nervous at all. This optimism was now gone and it was returning back home that I now felt uprooted. This must be how refugees feel.

While we were en route heading north, my daughter called up my granddaughter to let her we were on our way. My granddaughter said she had spoken to us and already knew we were on our way. When she was talking to her aunt she felt that a communication break down contributed to everything coming off the rails in Philly. Pat's daughter also called my grand-daughter and offered to help her "get rid of us" when we arrived. My grand-daughter told her, as long as she had a roof over her head, Pat and I had a roof over ours. My granddaughter never held the view that Pat should be institutionalized like Pat's daughters did. Unfortunately, there were now significant rifts within the family. Pat had told me a long time ago to say what you mean and mean what you say. I put this into practice when raising my granddaughter. As a result we always knew where each other stood. We could have diametrically opposed views on some issues, but still got along. Sounds simple, doesn't it. It is not. A psychologist said something to us a few years ago that I would never forget. She said, "People have agendas...always." This is true in families and was certainly true from our experience with the medical system. We arrived at my granddaughter's house and I spent the next several weeks groping as to what to do next. We were truly in limbo. In the meantime, I started treating Pat with an fMRI/ultrasound unit and she was responding well. Her attitude lightened up a bit and old memories started bubbling to surface. However, the uncertainty that was hovering over us was cancelling out some of the gains from the treatments. The anxiety of what the future held for us was harder on Pat than it was on me. My biggest fear was what we would do if Pat should need medical care. We were back in the town where all the medical and professional troubles started and it wasn't possible for her to receive unbiased care. The protocols for blood tests to monitor her iron levels and liver imaging would have to be put on hold.

My granddaughter was planning to attend college in Ontario for the fall of 2016. When we were getting ready to leave Atlantic Canada in 2103, Ontario was a place I was willing to consider. It wasn't my first choice, but if we had to remain in Canada it could be the best option. Pat on the other hand wasn't interested in Ontario. She had worked and lived in several Ontario cities in her twenties and didn't like any those experiences. I had lived and travelled from coast to coast in Canada, but not in Canada's largest province, but I was willing to keep an open mind about it. I tend to weigh one option against the other to arrive at the best decision. At the very least, I would know if Ontario would be a viable alternative. We talked things over with my granddaughter and decided we would all move to Ontario. There was a mutual benefit in going. The move would get Pat and I out of Atlantic Canada and we would be able to help my granddaughter out a lot so she wouldn't have to make such a big move alone. The winter of 2015 – 2016 saw over six feet of snow and by the time March rolled around the community's snow dumps were beyond capacity. We weren't sorry we were leaving this behind either.

Moving from Atlantic Canada to Mississauga was a momentous 1500-kilometre journey. We rented a moving truck and packed everything into it and we started the journey on March 30, arriving in Mississauga on April 2. I drove the moving truck and my granddaughter followed us with my car. It was by far the longest road trip she had ever had behind the wheel. We made arrangements to rent a town house online before leaving and when we arrived we unloaded everything into the attached garage. The choice of location was made for relative ease of access for my granddaughter to get to campus and for the amenities within a five-block radius. In walking distance was a shopping mall, grocery store, hardware store, a hospital, and across the street a high school that had an aquatic centre. Directly across the street from our town house was the high school's outdoor track and field including basketball courts. We spent the next several weeks getting the town house organized and getting Ontario driver licences, health cards and getting the utilities including the much-needed internet connection. The greatest obstacle was getting my older model car to meet Ontario's emissions standards. However, the real priority was to get Pat's health cards so we could find her a doctor and resume the quarterly blood tests for iron and the semi-annual liver imaging back on track.

I was curious to start exploring Toronto. The greater Toronto area is home to about 6.5 million people and is Canada's largest city. My impression of Toronto was primarily of it being Canada's centre of commerce and business, but was culturally boring. However, with a population base of this size I could easily have been wrong. Pat had never liked Toronto, but was willing to tolerate it in order to get out of Atlantic Canada. It took about three months for me to realize that the Toronto area never would be a home to us. First was the cost of housing. Toronto can be as expensive as New York City. Another big problem is that the GTA (greater Toronto area) doesn't have the infrastructure to support the population base. We started out several times to travel from Mississauga to Toronto to attend an event only to turn around and go home because of traffic congestion. Public transportation in the GTA was a patchwork of different providers that was awkward and time-consuming. Since it's difficult to travel to different areas of the GTA, many people do not travel outside of their neighbourhood. East of the Don Valley and the west end were two different worlds. The other reason that we moved was to be closer to Pat's oldest daughter and some other family members who lived in Toronto. Her daughter didn't drive and the inadequate transit system made it difficult for her to come out and visit us. Conversely, the difficulty of driving into the city and finding parking resulted in very few opportunities to get together. I looked into getting some music gigs, but that was pretty much a dead end as well. For contrast, I played five songs at a house concert in Philadelphia and was paid 100 USD. In Toronto I played a two-hour gig at a restaurant and was paid a paltry 40 CDN. I was fortunate to even get that because many venues were now hosting open mic nights where musicians would play a couple of songs and be paid nothing. This was frustrating to veteran musicians and younger musicians trying to make a living plying their craft.

Once the health cards arrived, it was time to find Pat a new doctor. We found one and he seemed like a nice enough guy, but, even though the Alzheimer's diagnosis had been debunked, he still went with the Alzheimer's diagnosis. This is when I realized the AD diagnosis would never be expunged from her chart and would permanently haunt her. We had another problem. Recall that we had liver imaging done at a private MRI clinic in Halifax and an ultrasound of Pat's liver at Hahnemann hospital in Philadelphia. In both cases, neither of these radiologists were given a heads-up about the cirrhotic liver nor did they see any indication of liver cirrhosis. The MRI and ultrasound summaries were three pages long and thorough. Pat's new family doctor arranged for Pat to have an ultrasound of her liver. The new radiologist was given a heads-up about cirrhotic liver tissue and that's what he saw. His report was one sentence long! What the hell is going on here? Her new doctor was willing to accept the bogus Alzheimer's diagnosis, but he totally ignored the discrepancy of the liver imaging. Soft tissue imaging is highly interpretive, but this didn't explain why her new doctor chose to ignore the imaging results from a prestigious hospital like Hahnemann. Then it dawned on me. He didn't work with the radiologists at Hahnemann; he worked with this local guy. I knew from past experience how hospital communities work. He went along with this radiology report so as to not rock the boat. He should have consulted the local radiologist about the discrepancy, but he didn't. So much for his living up to his responsibility for being Pat's advocate. He chose to look out for his own interests instead.

Pat and I would go for walks. Our neighbourhood was a planned community and the streets were in a grid rather than the maze that was the old Fishtown neighbourhood in Philadelphia. Pat can be so stubborn and she eventually wanted to walk by herself again. I worried about her walking alone after the Philadelphia fiasco. Sometimes she would walk laps on the big open track across the street where I could easily see her. If she went for a walk in the neighbourhood, I followed from a distance and she consistently found her way back home. This went on for a several months and eventually I didn't always follow her. Then one day she failed to return. Here we go again! Several hours went by and her daughter once again through phone calls found her at the hospital a couple of blocks away. It was unclear why the police picked her up and took her to the emergency room. Once again she was handcuffed for "her protection". I was getting fed up with her being treated this way. Pat used to do medicals for serving RCMP members and now she was afraid of police. How she was treated by the police was bad enough, but the legal means by which they took her into custody was far more disconcerting. She was placed under arrest using Canada's Mental Health Act. When I got back home I got online and looked into the Canadian Mental Health Act. I was shocked at the draconian powers contained within it. People who are subjected to the Act completely lose all basic civil liberties. People can face forced confinement and can be forced to take pharmaceuticals without consent. This is scary stuff. Pat's new doctor believed the bogus diagnosis of Alzheimer's disease and his opinion would hold great weight with any authorities. The medical system and physician governing bodies would all back him up. This is an incredible scenario. Law enforcement agencies taking their directives from a government-run monopoly health care system making serious misdiagnoses. This literally expose patients to extraordinary risks that could decimate their lives.

When I arrived at the emergency room, Pat was sitting calmly and even smiling. One reason that the police took her to the emergency room was that they couldn't get her name out of her. This is the same thing that happened in Philadelphia. I would find out a possible reason for this only a couple of weeks later. After a few hours at the emergency room, Pat was released and an appointment was made with a neurologist for follow up out patient care. Pat also was interested in starting counselling again. As in Philadelphia, it took a few phone calls to find a psychologist that was willing to work with Pat and her speech problems. We also thought it would be worth a try to resume speech therapy as well. Counselling and speech therapy were not covered by the government medical system and we would have to pay for these services out of pocket. We found a counsellor first and she knew of a speech therapist and a meeting was arranged to meet the therapist at the counsellor's home. The speech therapist made a good first impression with us. She seemed passionate about her work and after a few sessions we found that she was quite a bit more knowledgeable than the therapist back in Philadelphia. She requested all brain imaging summaries and assessments prior to starting sessions.

We were hoping some good would come from all this; however, a concern arose from the very first appointment with the counsellor. She wanted us to sign a consent that gave her freedom to talk to Pat's other health care providers. From what I had recently learned about the Canadian Mental Health Act, this sounded alarm bells in my head right away. Allowing cross-consultations with other health care providers had the potential of setting up a de facto committee. We already had a lot of experience with incorrect diagnoses and the harm that came from it. A de facto committee of several health care providers all agreeing on an incorrect diagnosis could result in disaster. Health care providers are beholden to governing bodies and their respective professional colleges ahead of the patients they treat. Pat and I wanted the freedom to make own choices whether they were right or wrong. I called up one of our doctor friends back in Atlantic Canada about my concern. He was a primary care physician that had done some counselling work in Ontario for two years. He advised us against agreeing to this. He agreed with me that this arrangement could expose Pat to the loss of her individual liberty. We didn't sign the consent. In just a few appointments, I knew we had made the right decision. The psychologist was jumping to conclusions about Pat that I knew were wrong. In the short term, a counsellor may be able to offer some suggestions or coping techniques, but it takes a long-term relationship for a counsellor to know a patient to avoid incorrect assessments. This exposes a significant weak spot if you get a counsellor who doesn't take the time to get to know their patient or, worse yet, a counsellor that thinks they know what's good for you and you don't.

The speech therapist on the other hand was very interesting. The first appointment was a review of the imaging reports that we had provided. She noted the small lacuna infarct in the area of the brain just behind Pat's right ear. This was in the same area where Pat struck her head when we were rear-ended coming off the George Washington Bridge in NYC a few years earlier. No one had ever told me, including Pat, that a lacuna infarct could mean stroke. I wanted Pat to be seen at the time when we were rear-ended, but she opted to see her own doctor after we got home. However, her doctor told her not to worry about it and no investigations were ordered. She did nothing. To the speech therapist, Pat's speech problems were classic signs of a stroke. The therapist used visual aids working with Pat. She would write in large print on a piece of paper what she just said or sometimes just key words and hold them up for Pat to read and repeat. I noticed when she turned away to write something else that her hand holding up the piece of paper would wander a bit. A little later she commented that Pat seemed to be able to read better from the left side of her field of vision. Her hand wasn't wandering at all; she was actually checking her field of vision. Interesting. She brought up a possibility that hadn't even occurred to me. Pat may be hearing muddled as well as speaking muddled. Another interesting possibility that she raised was that Pat may be having a hard time answering a question while at the same time she would have no problem providing the same information on her own accord. This involved two different neural pathways at work. This may explain why Pat failed to give her name when asked by the police, but a little later calmly told them her name unsolicited. Fascinating. These two possibilities may explain some of her behaviour and the inappropriate responses that frustrated me and the family. None of the neurologists we had seen in the last five years ever mentioned this to us. She also suggested that we watch some videos of the Arizona congress woman who suffered a gun shot to the head. The congresswoman had great difficulty in correctly naming objects. She would give wild answers like calling a chair a television. She knew what the object was but couldn't find the right word. Pat had been using word replacement for some time now but not to this extreme. Pat would sometimes point to her head and say that she knew it in here but couldn't get the words out. One of the techniques used to restore the congresswoman's speech (and most of her speech was restored) was to use music. There are localized areas in the brain for speech, but singing uses both hemispheres of the brain, bringing more of its own resources to bear. We read another example of a music teacher in Ottawa who used speech/music to restore her speech after brain surgery for an aneurysm. Using music in speech therapy was a relatively new method that required additional training which the therapist didn't have. We learned a lot from her. Neurologists should be working hand in hand with therapists instead of prescribing drugs to control behaviour and running useless tests like EEGs that lead to nothing useful.

Then came the outpatient appointment with the neurologist. Since we had provided Pat's new family doctor's name, the neurologist had a heads-up about the Alzheimer's disease diagnosis in her chart. I told him that this diagnosis had been debunked by a highly trained psychologist and the prominent Alzheimer's researcher in Philadelphia. Despite this he was still going to assume Pat had AD. Unbelievable and frustrating. Pat was now permanently branded with a disease she didn't have. This "branding" was going to expose Pat to some very dangerous medical care in the next couple of years. The appointment started with the neurologist asking Pat some questions. She was having a hard time answering, which didn't surprise me because Pat was now very nervous in any kind of clinical environment. Her speech problem worsened when she was anxious.

I tried to reassure Pat by telling her to try to relax. The neurologist asked me why I thought Pat's issue was just anxiety. Why was he assuming that I thought Pat's speech impediment was only an anxiety issue? This neurologist was expecting me to disregard the far more credible and knowledgeable sources that Pat didn't have AD. I wasn't in denial; it was doctors like him who were ignoring experts from their own medical community. I was guilty of not blindly accepting a discredited diagnosis and no amount of indignation from a doctor for my noncompliance was going to change that. I was getting fed up with denial accusations and I was also getting fed with explaining myself to doctors who were clearly biased. My goal was and always had been to get an accurate diagnosis so that Pat could get treated properly.

I tried explaining to the neurologist that I and other family members noticed that Pat stammered more when she was nervous. Even the speech therapist that Pat was working with noticed this. I also pointed out that when Pat talks about something she is enthusiastic about her stammer diminishes. His response was, "Ok, get her to talk about something she's enthusiastic about." This guy was a condescending asshole. When I recounted this to one of our family members who was also a doctor, her reaction was, "How old is this guy?" She thought this was really bad bedside manner. The appointment just continued to go down hill from there. I pointed out that brain imaging over the last few years showed no further brain atrophy and lesions, which should indicate that AD was an incorrect diagnosis. He said he had many patients who had severe brain atrophy and lesions that did not have Alzheimer's disease! I was stunned. That statement completely contradicted all the previous neurologists that we had seen in the last five years. This really threw me for a loop. I was always told that further atrophy of Pat's brain would support the Alzheimer's diagnosis. This was an important benchmark for me and this neurologist was calling this into question. Now who in the hell am I supposed to believe? What was I supposed to do now, flip a fucking coin? However, it was the next appointment that drove the last nail in the coffin for this guy.

At the next appointment, I brought up the possibilities that the speech therapist mentioned. Pat may be hearing muddled as well as speaking muddled. I asked him if he was taking that into consideration when he asked Pat questions. He didn't answer that directly, but mumbled some theories about neurology. How could a neurologist determine if an inappropriate response from a patient is the result of "hearing muddled" or due to broken neural pathways from brain disease? I brought up the other possibility that the speech therapist mentioned: Pat may have difficulty answering a question but could provide the same information unsolicited. The therapist's explanation was there were two different neural pathways involved. He said he was aware of that as well. This neurologist knew of the two issues that the speech therapist raised, but failed to mention anything to me. Not one neurologist in the last five years ever mentioned these possibilities that could have helped us immensely in managing our day-to-day lives. Knowing about these possibilities could have avoided a lot of misunderstanding and frayed tempers. We had to learn this from a speech therapist. It is my opinion that neurologists are clinically useless. If a doctor can't provide useful information for a patient to manage their lives when suffering a health issue, what good are they? Doctors try to resolve a patient's health issue and by extension try to provide help for a patient to manage their suffering. This appointment was a turning point and I saw no reason in seeing this guy anymore. I was fed up. This was the last neurologist we ever saw.

This was essentially the end of the line for mainstream medicine for us. We had given them five years and they were failures. I had been interested in what alternative medicine may have to offer, so we started shopping for a naturopath practitioner. We interviewed six of them. I may add that this would be all out of pocket because none of this was covered by the government single-payer system here in Canada.

We wanted to start by investigating for heavy metal toxicity. Only two of the naturopaths used chelation therapy. Chelation therapy is a method to rid the body of heavy metal toxins. We had already experienced five years of a dysfunctional mainstream medical system so we did far more due diligence in accepting an alternative medical approach. We would find that many of the alternative therapies had more logic and science behind them than much of the mainstream medicine we tried. There are also a lot of dead ends in the alternative medicine industry and outright fraud. You have to be cautious.

DEAD END OR A FORK
IN THE ROAD

This hope is self sustaining. It doesn't need you; you need it. Little by little, it reveals itself and you become more and more thirsty for the promise that it holds

We were five years into this medical odyssey and without much to show for it. This odyssey was tainted from the beginning by a politically driven diagnosis from the corrupt hospital where Pat had worked for decades. Despite the Alzheimer's diagnosis being overturned by two of the world's leading researchers on the subject, the doctors that we encountered still went with it and did not investigate for other possible answers. Over the next few years, I would also find that many doctors opinions contradicted their own regulatory bodies and their own medical academia. I had always held skepticism about the medicine that Pat was receiving, but I had no other frame of reference to compare it to. Frankly, I was willing to walk away from mainstream medicine for some time, but Pat was hesitant. After five years of ineffectiveness and fraud, she finally decided to try something else. At this point, I had no confidence or respect for the medical system and my opinion was only going to get worse over the next three years. We started looking into the alternative medical treatments and found some that had sound science behind them and also made common sense.

I had read a bit about mercury toxicity from dental amalgams and our inquiries started with this. Pat was due to have a teeth cleaning and her daughter provided us with her dentist's phone number. We called and made an appointment. She was a nice lady and I asked her what she thought about mercury toxicity from amalgam tooth fillings. She smiled and said that the World Health Organization deemed amalgams to be low risk. Not knowing any better, an endorsement from the WHO gave amalgams legitimacy to my eyes. The conversation turned to small talk as we compared stories about our travel adventures. She said she was taking a trip to Sweden with her son and "Oh, by the way, Sweden has outlawed the use of dental amalgams because they were afraid that dental waste material could end up in the water supply." I didn't challenge her on it, but couldn't help but wonder how she rationalized the safety of dental amalgams with this obvious contradiction. Now that we were going to start investigating for solutions outside the medical system, we were going to be far more discerning and try for a higher degree of due diligence. There is an old expression: "once burned, twice shy". When we got back home, I got online and started looking at what the World Health Organization had to say about mercury/amalgam fillings.

The World Health Organization in 2009 released a report recognizing dental amalgams as a significant source of mercury toxicity and recommended phasing out its use. The WHO further stated that amalgam filling are the primary source of mercury exposure in the general population and included mercury in its top ten list of chemicals considered a major health concern. The WHO's conclusions were based on human studies and laboratory experiments done on animals with amalgam fillings. Some of their studies indicate that there may be no safe level of exposure to mercury. Mercury released from amalgams can take several forms. Amalgams contain elemental mercury and can release mercury vapour, mercury ions and particles of mercury. When I raised the concern about possible mercury toxicity with a family member, she said that the mercury in amalgams is chemically bound and does not release mercury vapour. Her father was a dentist. Many people hold this common belief despite warnings from organizations like the WHO. I would find out later that the mercury in dental amalgams does indeed "gas off". Approximately 80 percent of inhaled mercury vapour from amalgams enters the blood stream through the lungs. Mercury vapour, mercury particles and mercury ions can also be swallowed and enter the gastrointestinal tract. Mercury can transform into vapour just at room temperature and the higher temperature in a person's mouth releases more. Increased temperature from hot drinks or friction from brushing teeth and chewing gum will increase even more mercury vapour into a person's system. The WHO acknowledges that mercury toxicity can cause damage to the nervous, digestive and respiratory systems. Health effects can include tremors, vision and hearing problems, emotional problems, attention deficits and fetal developmental deficits during pregnancies. Mercury in elemental form is lipid soluble, which results in mercury deposits being retained in body tissues. Most significantly, it can also cross the blood/brain barrier and be retained in brain tissues. Mercury can cross the placental barrier in pregnant women, exposing the fetus to mercury toxicity. Mercury has been found in a nursing mother's milk. Some evidence suggests that inorganic mercury can damage DNA. With these risk factors, how could mercury have been used as a dental filling for over a hundred years? The dentist's claim that the WHO deemed mercury a safe material for dental fillings wasn't sounding accurate to me. There are dentists who do have concerns about mercury fillings and will not use it. I thought I would now go see what Health Canada had to say about mercury.

On Health Canada's website, I found the use of mercury fillings had been controversial from as far back as 1845. Surveys even in recent years still revealed that over half of the population have concerns about the use of amalgams. Major print and television media have called into question the safety of amalgam tooth fillings. Pat's dentist was correct that Sweden had discontinued the use of amalgams, but so had Germany. Germany had prohibited amalgams for pregnant women, children and people with kidney disease for some time and eventually discontinued its use entirely. The University of Calgary had done experiments implanting amalgams in sheep's teeth. The amalgams in these experiments had radioactive markers to track where mercury travelled in their bodies. Mercury quickly appeared in major organs, especially the kidneys, impairing function by as much as 60 percent. Dental filling materials fall into the category of medical devices, but have been "grandfathered" in and are exempt from regulations enforced by the Food and Drug Act. Health Canada agreed with the WHO that most exposure to mercury toxicity is from the vapour emitted from amalgams. They acknowledge that mercury can be retained in the kidneys, brain, lungs, liver and gastrointestinal tract. Health Canada found that mercury levels in the blood and urine went down to the safe limits of 100 micrograms per gram of creatinine in urine after amalgams have been removed. However, I found a few paragraphs down they contradict themselves by stating that kidney function can be impaired by half that exposure limit. Health Canada further contradicts itself when it postulates that there may be no safe limit to mercury exposure. Regardless of contradictions on safe limits, Health Canada uses benchmarks based on mercury exposure from industry. There are few studies on continuous low-level exposure to mercury from amalgams which could render their benchmarks inaccurate. There needs to be studies done for low exposure to mercury because the signs of mercury toxicity are subtle and the symptoms can be wrongly diagnosed as something else. Some of Pat's creeping symptoms started developing years ago and we didn't pay attention to it. If we had been aware of mercury toxicity, we may have been able to take steps to eliminate or avoid a brewing health problem. There are specific studies that show Alzheimer's sufferers have higher levels of mercury in their brains, so the connection between cognitive deficits and mercury toxicity should not be overlooked. Some variables that make it difficult to determine safe levels for mercury toxicity are the different forms of mercury, different rates of absorption and excretion and the different metabolic pathways into the body. Despite the lack of thorough studies, the modelling simulators used by Health Canada still indicated that 50 percent of mercury exposure to humans comes from amalgam fillings. I thought I would now see what the US's Centers for Disease Control and Prevention and the Environmental Protection Agency had to say about mercury.

The following is gleaned from the Centers for Disease Control and Prevention's fact sheet. Elemental mercury which is used in dental amalgams can also be found in air, water and soil. Some elemental mercury gets into the environment through coal and fossil fuel burning. Elemental mercury can be converted to inorganic mercury in the human body. Large amounts of ingested inorganic mercury can cause intestinal problems, affect kidney function and cause neurological disorders. There is consensus that organic mercury (also known as methyl mercury) found in fish is the most toxic form of mercury. Up to 90 percent is absorbed into the blood stream from the GI tract and can reach the brain, causing permanent damage. Kidneys and developing fetuses are particularly susceptible to mercury toxicity. The CDC has done studies measuring methyl mercury in the blood and urine and determined that a level of 85 µg/L was associated with early neuro-developmental effects. Their studies determined that the danger limit was 58 µg/L. Safe levels of mercury in the blood are still ongoing research. Again, the health effects of continuous low level exposure like in dental amalgams is unknown. The Environmental Protection Agency states the dental amalgams are made up of approximately 40 – 50 percent mercury. The other elements in amalgams are approximately 25 percent silver, and 25 – 35 percent blend of copper, zinc and tin. To me, this begs the question, why are amalgams commonly known as "silver fillings" when the largest component is mercury? An anecdotal story from the EPA serves as an example of the danger of amalgam tooth fillings. A gentleman was melting dental amalgam in a casting furnace in the basement of his home to recover the silver. Mercury fumes released during the operation entered air ducts in the basement and circulated throughout the house. He along with his entire family suffered serious health consequences from the exposure. For a contrasting opinion, I now turned to the International Academy of Oral Medicine and Toxicology.

The International Academy of Oral Medicine and Toxicology is a non-profit organization. This group had far more information from a variety of sources on mercury toxicity than the WHO or Health Canada. They hold the contrasting opinion that amalgam fillings should be discontinued immediately for public safety and for the harm that mercury toxicity causes to the environment. The IAOMT found that mercury not only gasses off the filling but also leeches into the gums and bone. In addition to mercury being retained in the brain, liver, kidneys, lungs and gastrointestinal tract, the IAOMT cites studies show mercury toxicity can cause or exacerbate cardiovascular problems, hearing loss, Alzheimer's disease, autism, depression, antibiotic resistance, anxiety, Parkinson's disease, reproductive dysfunction and suicidal ideation. The IAOMT claims that up to 80 percent of mercury vapour is inhaled and once it's in the blood stream it can be distributed to several organs, which explains the wide range of symptoms. The half life of mercury in the whole body is estimated at fifty-eight days except for the brain. The half life of mercury in the brain can be decades. One problem with mercury toxicity is that it mimics so many ailments, but is rarely considered the primary source or primary contributor to diseases in mainstream medicine. The US National Institutes of Health attribute over 250 specific symptoms of mercury toxicity. Even though the United Nations is encouraging the reduction in the use of mercury including dental amalgams, it is still heavily used in dentistry. It's estimated there are 1000 tons of mercury in the mouths of Americans. The IAOMT had an interesting video library. It included videos from the faculty of medicine at the University of Calgary. Their medical department found that mercury vapour produced lesions in brain similar to 80 percent of the lesions found in an Alzheimer's brain. Their experiments combined mercury ions with brain neurons in a petri dish. Brain neurons look similar to branches on a tree to me. One of the structural proteins is called tubulin and they connect end to end, forming like a sheath for underlying neurofibrils. When mercury ions were introduced into the petri dish, the binding sites for these proteins broke down, rendering them unable to connect. This stripped the underlying neurofibril components of the outer layer of tubulin and the neurofibrils shrivelled up, causing lesions similar found in the brain of Alzheimer's patients. The experiment also tried adding other heavy metals ions like aluminum, lead, cadmium and manganese, but these metals did not have this effect, only mercury ions. Low levels of mercury ions were used in the experiment, which would be similar to the low levels that would be gassing off from mercury dental amalgams. These are medical experiments done by mainstream medicine's own academia that most doctors are completely unaware of.

Not all patients will experience the same symptom or combination of symptoms because individuals can react to mercury exposure in ways that are unique to their own bodies. The World Health Organization estimates mercury intake in the general public is 1 to 27 μg of mercury every day. This exceeds California's EPA safety range and affects millions of people daily. The Occupational Safety and Health Administration also supports the concept of delayed reactions to mercury toxicity. Many chronic diseases can take twenty to thirty years to develop symptoms. A study revealed that 3.9 percent of those tested have allergic reactions to heavy metal exposure. If this is true, millions of people are unknowingly allergic to mercury. If these people should suffer the adverse health effects from the mercury toxicity, mainstream medicine is more likely to diagnose the symptoms as having been caused by something else.

Another factor that we had read about was the possible relationship between Alzheimer's disease and the APOE gene (Apo-lipoprotein). There are three variations of the APOE gene, APOE 2, 3, and APOE 4. As with other genes, we inherit a copy from each of our parents. If you inherited the APOE 2 variant, your chances of developing Alzheimer's-like symptoms are very low. If you inherited APOE 4 then your chances of developing these symptoms are much higher. Mainstream medicine recognizes the risk factors from these genes, but most of the attention in AD research is the relationship between this gene and the amyloid and the tau proteins. What I found from links through the IAOMT is the relationship between the APOE gene and mercury toxicity. The APOE gene is sort of a housekeeping gene and its job is to carry away oxidized lipids and cholesterol from the brain. The APOE 2 has a strong sulphur binding site that can bind to mercury and carry it away. This is a possible explanation as to why patients who inherited a copy of APOE 2 from both of their parents have a much lower potential of coming down with AD-like symptoms. Mainstream research does not consider this role of the APOE gene and mercury toxicity. However, research needs funding and like it or not, the flow of research dollars is directed by agendas which does not include the toxic effects of mercury on human health.

So what did I learn from all this information? The WHO, Health Canada, Centers for Disease Control and Environmental Protection Agency had too many contradictory positions to draw any definitive conclusions. The International Academy of Oral Medicine and Toxicology had much more information and a broader perspective that shed more light than the regulatory agencies. Of particular importance to Pat's health was the fact that mercury can cross the blood/brain barrier and the mercury can be retained in brain tissue for years. How could regulatory agencies allow the use of mercury in dental fillings when they hadn't completed any studies to determines its safety? After all, these agencies had had over 150 years to determine the safety of amalgams and failed to do so. Mercury is in the top ten list of known neuro-toxic substances in the world and some sources classify it in the top three neuro-toxic substances. Allowing this substance to be used simply doesn't make any sense. This was only the beginning of our journey outside mainstream medicine and the next few years would reveal more about how we couldn't place blind trust in the regulatory side of the medical/industrial complex.

Time and time again the consistent question that arose from medical professionals was: where did Pat get the mercury from? This question always caught me flat footed and I had no answer. I had grown accustomed to doctors repeating talking points that they had no direct knowledge of and questions as to where the mercury came from was just another example of rhetorical group think. Talking points and rhetorical questions effectively serve as a deflection and disinformation whether it's intentional or not. To be fair, doctors are not researchers and they should be able to rely on regulatory agencies, but not to the point where they abandon their own common sense. There are some doctors and other medical professionals who do question the safety of drugs and medical devices, but not enough. It takes courage to speak out because questioning the medical/industrial complex can be career ending. There are several sources that can expose the general public to mercury toxicity and the information is readily available for anyone to find including the medical community. The World Health Organization says that 53 percent of mercury emissions come from the medical industry itself. When a doctor asks where the mercury toxicity came from, they didn't need to look any further than themselves.

Where did Pat get the mercury from was a good question, so I decided to look. As it turns out, there are many sources for mercury toxicity. Sources for mercury toxicity is a far more ubiquitous in the environment than regulatory agencies care to acknowledge. For most people fish consumption comes to mind. Large predator fish that are higher up the food chain have higher accumulation of mercury and are to be most avoided. A good rule is, if a fish is too big to fit in your frying pan, don't eat it. The Atlantic Ocean is a massive body of water, so just what is the concentration of mercury in its waters that prompts warnings about fish consumption and how did it get there? I knew about restricting salmon consumption for some time, but it came as a surprise to me that there were also advisories for eating brook trout. Rivers, brooks and streams are far smaller bodies of water than the North Atlantic. Where was that mercury coming from? More to the point, brooks and streams are part of the environment that humans live in. If the fish in our neighbourhoods are toxic, could people be exposed to the same sources? I found a PhD environmental scientist who said that there is extensive statistical information on the toxicity levels in wildlife and virtually no studies on toxic exposures in humans. This environmental scientist had become mercury toxic himself and realized that the lack of studies on the health risks from environmental toxins for humans is unacceptable.

Then I heard about Grassy Narrows First Nations reservation in northern Ontario. The Grassy Narrows reserve had an ongoing mercury toxicity problem for over fifty years. The source of the mercury toxicity came from a pulp and paper mill that had dumped ten tons of mercury over its years of operation from 1962 to 1970. The mercury leached into the water ways and contaminated the fish, a staple food source for the reserve's inhabitants. The sport fishing industry was a major source of income for the reserve and it was decimated as well. The tragedy of the Grassy Narrows reserve drew the attention of the Japanese. A Japanese research team was dispatched to study the problem. The Japanese call mercury poisoning Minamata disease. This disease was discovered in 1956 in the Japanese community of Minamata. The inhabitants of the community suffered one of the most severe cases of mercury toxicity ever documented. A nearby chemical factory had dumped mercury in the local waters for thirty-six years, poisoning the fish. Pulp and paper has been an industry in Atlantic Canada for decades. One of our family members has an environmental science degree and he said the standard practice for the pulp and paper industry to dispose of its mercury was to simply bury it. No one knows how much mercury was disposed of in this manner and no one knows how much mercury contamination is in the environment. So where did the mercury come from? It would seem from these above examples that environmental mercury toxicity is very common in areas that use mercury or had used it for industrial purposes. If this is so, then it would good public health policy and a preventative health measure in knowing the level of mercury toxicity in the general public like the environmental scientists know about the birds and fishes.

This is all baffling to me. Mercury is a known neuro-toxin and its detrimental health effects have been known for over a hundred years. My granddaughter stumbled upon an anecdotal story about mercury toxicity. She went with her college class on a field trip to a textile museum. There she learned about a disease called erethism, also known as the mad hatter disease. To me the Mad Hatter was a character in Lewis Carroll's book *Alice's Adventures in Wonderland*. Mercury was used in treating animal fur in the making of hats. The workers that were exposed to the inorganic mercury started exhibiting several symptoms as a result of the toxic effects on their central nervous systems. Behavioural changes were observed that included irritability, low self-confidence, depression, apathy and personality changes.

One of the things that stood out to me was the amalgams had approximately 40 – 50 percent mercury. If the major component is mercury then why are amalgams commonly known as "silver fillings"? Why aren't they called mercury fillings? I'm being facetious. Most people know that mercury is poisonous and revealing mercury as the primary component in amalgams wouldn't be a good selling point. We knew enough now about mercury toxicity that it was worth investigating to see if it was a contributor to Pat's health problems.

ROLLER COASTERS AND REVELATIONS

All at once...the bubble burst. It burst...and my sense of what had been real came spilling out all over the floor like the guts of a slaughtered animal

I tend to overthink. Since I don't have a medical degree, I am not sure what I'm looking for, so I look at everything. When doctors repeatedly asked where Pat got the mercury from, the thought that crossed my mind was, "You're the doctor and that's for you to determine." Optimally we all want as clear and definitive information that we can find to make medical decisions. Opposing opinions from the medical community were an experience I had many times and the topic of mercury was no different. One dentist says amalgams are safe; another dentist feels mercury fillings should be outlawed immediately. Mercury is a known neurotoxin and the safety of its use was not established, so we decided to find out if Pat was mercury toxic. There was no point in pursuing mainstream medicine to investigate this because they didn't "believe" that mercury was a problem in the general population. For this, we decided to go to a naturopath practitioner to see if we could get an answer.

We made appointments with six different naturopaths for a free initial consultation. Only two of the naturopaths did chelation therapy. Chelation therapy is a chemical process to remove heavy metals from body tissue. If a urinalysis tested positive for mercury toxicity, then she would need to start a chelation program to drain the mercury from her body. The province of Ontario recognizes chelation therapy and requires that it be done under the supervision of a doctor. We tried to cross-reference alternative medical treatments with mainstream medicine as much as possible to make the best decisions. The government's medical system may have recognized chelation therapy, but medical doctors weren't interested in supervising. Naturopaths just went about their business on their own using chelation in treating their patients.

One of the two naturopaths that used chelation therapy had been an ambulance technician in the past, so we decided to go with him. The first step was for Pat to have a heavy metal test to determine if she had metal toxicity. He gave us a urine collection kit for us to take home. This was interesting. Urine samples at a doctor's office are usually collected by providing the patient with a small bottle and they go to the washroom right at the doctor's office. The urine sample for the naturopath was collected over a six-hour period at home with a chelating agent and drinking a lot of water. A chelating agent draws embedded mercury in body tissues, giving a more accurate measure of toxicity, otherwise only the mercury present in the urine would be measured. Each time she went to the bathroom, the urine was added to a one-litre container. This was a much higher average than the little bottle provided at a doctor's office. After the collection, the container was well shaken and frozen. The sample was packed up for shipping using ice packs and sent to an independent laboratory in Alberta. The laboratory was accredited by the College of Physicians and Surgeons. The College also regularly reviewed the lab's analytical data and did random physical inspections on site to ensure compliance with accepted laboratory practices. The College also made sure that there were no unsupported claims regarding the results and that samples were ordered by a regulated health care professional. The lab doing the urinalysis used the reference benchmarks from the US

Environmental Protection Agency. In all, sixteen other heavy metals were tested for besides mercury including lead.

While we were waiting for the results, the naturopath suggested for Pat start drinking a green tea extract to help reduce her iron levels. Pat enjoyed drinking herbal teas and knew that herbal remedies had medicinal use. She didn't have any training in herbal remedies, nor did she use in it in treating her patients, but she had read some abstracts about their medical benefits. There was no conclusive evidence that green tea was effective in reducing iron levels, but green tea is a well known anti-oxidant. The naturopath also started Pat on a round of homeopathic remedies as an aid in lowering Pat's iron levels. Homeopathy has been around since the 1700s and is controversial. It works on the principle that like attracts like, so, to reduce Pat's iron, a homeopathic ferrum formulation was used. This sounded strange to us, but considering the potentially horrific side effects of many pharmaceutical products she decided to go ahead and give this a try. Our only metric for medical treatments for us now was results. If over a reasonable amount of time we didn't feel that the results were achieved, then she would discontinue the treatment.

After a few weeks the results from the urinalysis came back. The naturopath called us and an appointment was made to go over the results. Pat's mercury levels were nine times higher than recommended safe levels. However, we were surprised to find her lead levels were eleven times higher. The naturopath had been in practice for thirteen years and had never seen mercury or lead levels this high with any of his patients. He started Pat on DMSA (dimercaptosuccinic acid), a common chelating agent for mercury and lead toxicity. DMSA is on the World Health Organization's list of essential medicines. Chelating for heavy metals would be pointless if the source for toxicity wasn't removed. The only known source for Pat's mercury poisoning was the mercury tooth fillings. The naturopath referred us to a dentist that didn't use amalgams and used safe practices for amalgam removal. Care needs to be taken for amalgam removal because this is when the release of mercury vapour and mercury particles is at its highest.

In the meantime we decided to take the urine results to Pat's primary care physician to see what his response would be. He was less than enthusiastic. We explained how the urine was collected and the lab was accredited and randomly inspected by the College of Physicians and Surgeons. Despite his reservations, he had the phlebotomist in his office draw blood and sent the sample to a toxicologist at the hospital. At the next appointment he told us the blood sample did not show any mercury toxicity. I didn't know what to think. I decided to look into the difference between a blood test versus a urine test for determining toxicities. A blood test only reveals mercury toxicity if there was a recent exposure. The blood tests detect mercury in the blood and not mercury that's embedded in body tissue. I didn't think of it at the time, but the doctor knew this. I know that he knew, because of Pat's hemochromatosis. Recall from the second chapter that the standard practice in mainstream medicine for determining a patient's iron overload is to measure the ferritin count. Ferritin is a protein that stores iron in body tissues and is a more accurate measure for iron overload, whereas an iron blood test only measures iron present in the blood. From this, he knew the difference between testing for toxins embedded in tissues versus testing for toxins in the blood. Also when I thought back about this, he didn't present us with a toxicology report. I have doubts if the blood he drew at his office ever went to a lab, let alone was assessed by a toxicologist. The reason I think this is because mainstream medicine does not believe mercury exposure comes from dental amalgams. He wouldn't have wasted a toxicologist's time with this and the toxicologist would have thought he was a fool for bringing this to him anyway. I've been around doctors and medicine long enough to think my assumption is probably correct. The primary care doctor also asked the rhetorical question, "where did she get the lead from?" He had me on that one. I had no idea. It was completely by chance that a few months later I would find out the likely source of Pat's lead poisoning. I was talking to a friend about Pat's urinalysis and the mystery of the lead poisoning and he told me something astonishing. He was in the construction business and one of his colleagues told him it was only in the year 2000 that his company removed the lead lining that was in the one of the large municipal water towers back in our hometown. I couldn't believe it, but this was the most probable source for Pat's lead toxicity. I had confidence in the urine sample that was ordered by the naturopath and I had confidence in the accredited laboratory that conducted the test. We would go with the urinalysis and disregard Pat's doctor.

We made an appointment with the dentist that the naturopath recommended to us. The initial consult was a visual inspection and X-rays were taken. The dentist provided us with ample information about the dangers of mercury fillings, including online links to help bring us up to speed on the subject before our next appointment. We reviewed the information he provided us and it made a strong case for the dangers of amalgam tooth fillings. Since Pat had a dental plan, there was no reason not to proceed and eliminate this possible source for mercury toxicity. At the next appointment, the dentist said imaging revealed there was some tooth decay hidden by the amalgam fillings and that it needed to be repaired anyway. I was a little surprised by this news. The previous dentist had taken images as well, but didn't tell us that there was tooth decay. This dentist said that amalgams can obscure tooth decay and extra discernment is needed when assessing imaging. The dentist wanted to remove the amalgams in three separate appointments. His strategy was based on his personal experience when he had had his amalgams removed. A lot of mercury is released when removing amalgams and, if proper precautions are not taken, there is a risk that the patient could suffer a toxic shock. This happened to him. Removing Pat's amalgams with three different appointments would reduce the risk of this happening. He went on to explain the precautions that he took. Where possible, he tried to remove the amalgam in one intact piece to reduce the risk of mercury vapour and mercury particles in the event that it broke apart. He used a dental dam for the patient and gave the patient a supply of oxygen during the procedure. When we arrived for the first appointment, the dentist and his assistant looked like they were wearing hazardous waste material gear to reduce their exposure as well. Avoiding mercury exposure was taken very seriously.

This all reminded me of a statistic I read once about the suicide rates for professionals. Consistently, physicians had the highest suicide rate, followed dentists. I saw first hand how practising medicine can be a pressure cooker, but why was the suicide rate so high for dentists? Dentist do not have anywhere near the stresses in their practice compared to physicians. However, dentists are heavily exposed to possible mercury toxicity from the work they do. Since many dentists do not believe that amalgam fillings are hazardous, they do not protect themselves from exposure. Pat's uncle was a dentist for years and brought something up in conversation once that I never forgot. He used the example of a person suffering a cardiac angina attack. A nitroglycerin tablet is placed under the tongue because that's one of the fastest entry points to the blood stream. Good dental hygiene was important because bad bacteria can enter a person's system the same way as well. Indeed, Pat had read in medical journals that bacteria could play a role in heart disease. Couldn't the mercury being released by dental amalgams be absorbed the same way? The answer would appear to be yes. These are the kind of things I think about and ask why.

The three appointments to remove the filling was spread out over three weeks. The dentist decided to remove the largest mercury filling first. The day after the removal all hell broke loose. Pat had a massive anxiety attack that lasted for four days. She was crying and was continually pacing around the house highly agitated. What the hell is going on? Removing the source for mercury toxicity was supposed to be a step toward improvement. Pat had serious anxiety spikes in the past that lasted a few hours, but not for days on end. We got through it, but it was touch and go and I thought an intervention might be needed. On the fifth day, the anxiety just stopped like it had never happened. This was one hell of an emotional roller coaster ride. I reported this to the dentist at the next appointment and he looked somewhat embarrassed. If there were no other factors that could explain the anxiety attack, then it would have to be attributed to a toxic shock from the mercury released during the removal. The description of Pat's anxiety attack seemed to confirm to him that this is what likely happened. He said the toxic shock he had when he had his amalgams removed was similar. In the absence of another explanation, I guess he was right. If he was right, Pat had mercury exposure despite the meticulous precautions he had taken to avoid this from occurring. The removal of the two other mercury fillings were uneventful. They came out with little effort and fully intact.

The naturopath had already warned us about toxic shock. The DMSA chelating agent he used was going to be in small doses to avoid this reaction. Pat would be taking it over several months to "drain" the mercury slowly that was embedded in body tissue. This reminded me of a movie I had seen that was based on actual events. Hollywood movies tend to over-dramatize, so I read up on the real story that the movie was based on. The story was about a father's fight to find a cure for his children who had a genetic disorder called Pompe disease. Children who had this disease usually did not survive past the age of ten. Pompe disease causes too much sugar being stored in body tissues. The result is progressive muscle weakness and damage to organs, particularly the heart, liver, skeletal muscle and the nervous system. A researcher developed an enzyme that was able to release the stored sugar avoiding damage. As the kids were receiving the treatment, they start, laughing uncontrollably. This confirmed that the treatment was working. The kids were laughing because of all the sugar that was being released from their body tissues. They were having a sugar high. The side effect of sugar being released is far less serious than a neurotoxin like mercury being released, but it does serve as an example of the effects of chelating.

I may overthink sometimes, but you have to go with what you know. I remembered from my college chemistry courses that all the elements have an electrical charge except the inert gases. Amalgam tooth fillings are composed of up to five different metals, each with an electrical charge, and amalgams are in the acidic environment of a person's mouth. So isn't this the making of a battery? Maybe. What is certain is that when two dissimilar metals come in contact an electrical current is produced. This is called a galvanic response and we usually see this a corrosion. The electrical currents produced by amalgams are stronger than the electrical activity produced in a person's brain. Just saying. It was a year later that Pat started seeing a functional medicine doctor. The short definition of a functional medical doctor is a regular MD who treats holistically. At the first appointment, he noticed that Pat had gold tooth filling. I told him that she had the mercury fillings removed. The functional medicine doctor claimed studies indicate that mercury fillings in the presence of gold can increase the uptake of mercury by a factor of 100. This is basic chemistry. Once again I was faced with rudimentary science being ignored by a medical community that prides itself on being scientific and evidence-based.

Two months after Pat had started the chelation program and had the mercury fillings removed, her anxieties were noticeably going down. It looked like results were being achieved. The spring before, her anxieties had been very high, so this was a welcome relief. She continued going for walks to alleviate her anxiety and she still stubbornly wanted to go by herself once in a while. If she took longer than fifteen minutes, I would go out and find her just to make sure she was alright. She was taking longer than I felt comfortable with on one of her walks so I went out to see where she was. I barely got out the door when I saw her running down the sidewalk toward home. I thought this was great because Pat used to like jogging and I thought she must be feeling good enough to start again. Then I noticed a police officer walking about a half block behind her. He was following her and she was running to get away from him. Great, not this crap again. She had almost reached me when the cop turned around and didn't see us go into our house. I peered out the window for the next hour and saw two police cruisers driving around our neighbourhood looking for her. We stayed inside and dodged a bullet. What a way to live.

As the next few months went by, Pat continued to incrementally improve, but Pat can be her own worst enemy sometimes. She keeps things to herself and tries to deal with it on her own, leaving those around her in the dark. I would notice once in a while that she wasn't always finishing meals and occasionally complained of stomach pain. This was a clue that I didn't pay enough attention to and then one day it happened. Her anxieties were revving up. I had seen this many times. She was pacing around the house and then she sat down and started crying. She started stomping her feet and then she blurted out, "IT HURTS!" I asked her, "What hurts?" She responded, "my belly." BOOM! I was instantly transported back in time. Several years ago Pat had used to complain about her gut. I asked my granddaughter if she remembered that too. She said, "Yeah, now that you mention it I remember all Pat wanted to eat was probiotic yogurt and drink prune juice?" Pat had stopped complaining about it long ago and we both had forgotten about it until now. Pat used to joke about how she wished she could go to the bathroom as easily as I do and I would joke about it, saying that's because I'm full of shit. I suggested at the time that she may want to get an investigation to see if something could be done about it. She just brushed it off. I don't know why, but many doctors have this "suck it up and deal with it" when it comes to their own health issues. I started paying attention to when Pat was agitated and I would ask her if her gut hurt. Most of the time the answer was yes. So many times, when the family and I thought Pat was having an anxiety attack, she was actually in pain.

The other thing I noticed was, when she was having gut pain, she wanted to go for a walk. This was a revelation to understanding her behaviour. I have hit my thumb with a hammer on several occasions and I would stomp around trying to "walk off" the pain. How could I have missed all this? Then again, who follows their partner into the bathroom to observe their toilet habits? I do not have gut issues, but a few years later I got a glimpse of what Pat was going through. I get migraines every so often, so I took one of Pat's painkillers that had been prescribed to her. One of the side effects of painkillers is constipation and my gut locked up solid. It felt like I was trying to pass a brick when I went to the bathroom. It hurt like hell and then I realized this was what Pat was going through on a daily basis. No wonder she wanted to "walk it off". Furthermore, she had been dealing with this for years now.

I went back and read the research papers on mercury toxicity. Sure enough, free mercury ions can cause digestive problems by interfering with the gut's digestive enzymes. Now that Pat was chelating for mercury, I was hoping this may help out her gut too. I also found out that the gut has far more neurons than there are neurons in the brain. And the gut also produces the neurotransmitters that the brain uses. There is also a gut/brain axis with bi-way communication between the two. Interesting. This means if there is gut dysfunction it also affects brain dysfunction. There seems to be an accepted example of this problem. Many autistic kids have gut dysfunction and, when this has been treated, autistic symptoms improve and there are cases where autistic symptoms are completely resolved. Treating gut dysfunction has also helped adults who have memory, mental health and cognitive problems. Wow! I thought we may be really on to something to help Pat. We brought this up with the naturopath at the next appointment and he started her on some supplements to restore the flora and fauna in Pat's gut.

After nine months of chelation therapy, Pat's anxiety decreased by about 70 – 80 percent. We could also see in her eyes that she was more "with it" and she more was attentive to conversations going on around her. However, we would discover other serious health issues that we didn't know about over the next two years. Our journey was far from over.

THE SEARCH FOR A NEW HOME

Some times you gotta lean
right into the grinding stone
forget about how things have been
and step into the unknown

In April 2016, the lease was up on our town house and the experiment of living in the greater Toronto area was over. It was three years ago that we sold our home in Atlantic Canada and we were ready to put down roots again. Not having a home base provided us with a sense of freedom that we needed at the time, but now it was an impediment to how we really wanted to live. My granddaughter still had another year of college, so we stayed for a couple of months longer to help her find another place to live before getting down to business of finding our new home. After years of living in the harsh Atlantic Canadian winters, we were interested in living in a warmer climate. Secondly, we were interested in living in a place that offered a lower cost of living. Of the places that we had travelled, a small town on the north shore of the Dominican Republic best fit these criteria. We had visited the village of Cabrera in the Dominican Republic and liked it there a lot. We decided to go back and give it a second look. I was concerned about how Pat would do on the trip. Air travel can be stressful getting through security and the waiting, but Pat handled the trip far better than I expected.

We were always interested in staying active and my granddaughter was interested in starting a business. We talked about partnering in an enterprise that could serve each of our agendas. We would be able to fund the start-up costs and my granddaughter could work the business becoming a full partner through sweat equity. Alternatively, she could work her way into full ownership and we could remain as investors until she owned the business outright. In reality, we didn't need much of an income stream from a business. It was more of a security blanket rather than an absolute necessity. Just having family close by was a big dividend for us. My granddaughter had never been to the Dominican Republic and she joined us a couple of weeks after our arrival to check the place out for herself. She can handle hot and dry climates like Mexico, but the humidity in DR was too much for her and wasn't going to work.

For years, our trips always pivoted around Pat attending physicians' continuing medical education courses. These were always held at all inclusive resorts. We never liked the all-inclusive experience and we would travel off resort for a more immersive experience of the culture. The tourist experience and living in a community as an expat are two different things. We also had to look at it through the lens of starting a business as well. Many of the expat "pensionados" spent most of their time in their gated communities and many did not venture outside the resorts. This presented a significant loss of a potential market for a business and most Dominicans do not have a lot of disposable cash. We didn't feel confident about staring a business there. The other thing that I had to admit to myself was that places like the DR can be fun and relaxing, but I really preferred a multi-cultural society like we have in North America. I liked having access to amenities like a good blues and ribs bar. We decided that the DR wasn't going to be a permanent home for us and we returned to Canada.

It was mid-June when we returned to Canada and we spent a week with my granddaughter before continuing on to our next adventure. We had travelled through Osoyoos, British Columbia in the early Nineties and had never forgotten it. The town is located in the southern tip of the Okanagan valley with a sunny and arid climate. Just the way we like it. It is in close proximity to the Canadian/US border, giving us easy access to US destinations. We left Toronto and drove north to Sault St. Marie, where we crossed the border into the states. I had driven from the east coast of Canada to the west coast many times and always preferred driving through the upper-tier states. We were retracing our earlier trip west and wanted to revisit the South Dakota Badlands and Mount Rushmore. On this trip we also included Devil's Tower in Eastern Wyoming and Yellowstone National Park to our points of interest. Devil's Tower was featured prominently in the movie *Close Encounters of the Third Kind* and is unique. We did a drive through of Yellowstone with one stop at the Old Faithful geyser. Yellowstone is at an altitude of 8000 feet and the temperature was cool enough for some snow flurries that day. It was too cool for Pat, so we didn't stay long. We got back on I-90 heading west and, when we got to Coeur d'Alene, Idaho, we turned north to cross back into Canada at Creston, British Columbia. From there we got on route 3 west all the way to Osoyoos.

Midway through the trip Pat was getting increasingly agitated. Pat needed to walk around to get her gut moving and the long hours sitting in the car had locked up her gut, causing her a great deal of pain. We tried to compensate by having her drink more fluids, increasing her intake of fibrous foods and adding some off-the-shelf probiotic supplements, but nothing really helped. It wouldn't be until the following year when Pat would make significant improvement in her gut function after we started working with a functional medicine doctor. For the time being she was very uncomfortable and dealing with the stress was a daily challenge. We found a motel room to be our base while we spent the next few weeks getting to know the town better. We felt while we drove all this way that we should also explore more of the valley and drove as far north as Kelowna. I lived in the Vancouver area in the late Eighties and it was very difficult to form a social life there. I thought a smaller community in the interior of British Columbia might be different, but it seemed to be the same. We had intended to do a thorough investigation of different areas of British Columbia, but decided against it and headed back east. Again, the long hours on the road were difficult for Pat and things came to head. We went to a hospital emergency room and got a prescription for lorazepam. Lorazepam belongs to a class of drugs called benzodiazepines and is prescribed for anxiety. The drug was able to settle her down enough for us to continue our travels.

When we were living in Toronto I was curious about the Lake Erie region. We had never gotten there so I thought we would take the opportunity to go through that area on our way back. We travelled east to Winnipeg, Manitoba, and then turned south to travel through the US again. My intent was to cross back into Canada at Detroit-Windsor and then drive along the Lake Erie shoreline. We crossed the Ambassador Bridge that links Detroit and Windsor, but instead of taking the 401 highway north we got on county road 20, which took us fairly close to Lake Erie and through the smaller towns. I really enjoy the small mid-west towns travelling through the states and the small towns through Essex county had the same look and feel. Around 6 o'clock in the evening we found a room for the night. The next morning we decided to stay for a couple of days and do some exploring. The town was a lakeside community surrounded by farmland and is Canada's most southern point. The terrain was very flat like the prairies, but with a lot of wooded areas. Over the years I learned not to ignore my intuitive sense and this place was feeling pretty good. I liked Essex county, but we continued on up the Lake Erie coastline, stopping at a few towns on the way. When we got to my granddaughter's apartment in Brampton, we spent a couple of days tidying up some business and made plans to return to Essex county as soon as possible. Spending a couple of days in Brampton reminded us of how much we disliked the GTA (greater Toronto area). When we got back, we got a room at the same family-owned motel that we had stayed at previously. The owners were very friendly and generous in providing what they knew about the area.

One month after Pat started taking the lorazepam prescription, she had a grand mal seizure. She never had a seizure in her life and there was no family history for seizures either. It happened at 5 in the morning. It scared the hell of me. I had never seen a grand mal seizure before. She let out a yell and her body went rigid and she was foaming at the mouth. I dialled 911 right away and they needed the civic number for the motel, but I didn't know it. One of the motel workers was living in the room next to us and I knew they were early risers, so I banged on their door. She gave me the civic number for the motel and I told the 911 dispatcher. I was in a panic. The 911 voice on the other end of the phone tried to calm me down and suggested that I talk to Pat. She said Pat may look unconscious, but was very likely able to hear and understand everything I was saying. The rigid part of the seizure lasted maybe half a minute and then she went totally limp for several minutes and was unresponsive. When the ambulance arrived Pat was starting to come around, but she was very groggy. They loaded her into the ambulance and took her to the local hospital. I followed. When I saw her in the emergency room she was fully awake and very agitated. We stayed in the emergency room for observation for about an hour and she eventually settled down. She was released and we went back to the motel.

The lorazepam prescription was the only new variable to enter our lives and I my suspicions went immediately to it. I didn't know anything about lorazepam, so I got online and started reading up on it. Lorazepam belongs to a class of drugs called benzodiazepines. Benzodiazepines modifies the activity of the neurotransmitter gamma-aminobutyric acid (GABA). GABA is an inhibitory neurotransmitter and "appears" to perform a regulatory function.

It affects several brain functions and research "suggests" GABA also helps in controlling fear and anxiety. Since mainstream medicine knows little about the brain, it should come as no surprise that they know very little about how "brain drugs" actually work. Monkeying around with the brain's natural neurotransmitters without knowing how the brain actually works is irresponsible to me. The standard practice for prescribing brain drugs is a matter of trial and error. Trial and error on the human brain? Your brain is the seat of your personality and controls autonomic functions like your heartbeat. I find it incredible that modern medicine is willing to experiment with drugs and then cross their fingers hoping that things will turn out right. By now for me, words like "appears", "suggests" and "trial and error" were all blaring alarm bells and were indications that they really have no idea what they were doing. One of the side effects of benzodiazepines is constipation. At the emergency room, when Pat was prescribed lorazepam, I told the emergency room doctor that she was having a lot of abdominal pain. So he prescribed a drug that can cause gut problems to help her deal with the stress and anxiety from her gut problems. I once again was asking myself, this is medicine?

As I researched benzodiazepines, I found something very disconcerting. Benzodiazepines are physically addictive. As patients develop a tolerance, higher dosages are required to maintain the desired effect. I found three former heroin addicts from online benzodiazepine groups who found it more difficult to quit benzodiazepines than it was to kick heroin! Originally, benzodiazepines were only intended for short-time use of a few weeks. Now it's common practice for doctors to renew prescriptions, keeping their patients on it for years. Some of the side effects from long term use of this drug are anxiety, panic attacks and agoraphobia. Tragically these symptoms are often blamed on the patient's original complaint and never the drug itself. This results in doctors increasing the dosage that dooms the patient to a downward spiral of physical dependence. The patient doesn't know that their worsening symptoms is due to the drug and they believe that they are just getting sicker.

It is highly recommended that patients use a tapering schedule to discontinue its use. Doctors follow the pharmaceutical industry's recommended tapering guide lines, but for many patients the taper is too quick and they suffer withdrawal symptoms. There were percipient doctors who questioned the safety and effectiveness of this drug and they took the time to work closely with patients to develop safe tapering programs. They recognized their patients were not all the same. There are other considerations like the different potencies of prescriptions, the metabolic rate from different manufacturers or a person's age. Benzodiazepines can cause confusion or memory loss and this has led many doctors to wrongly diagnose older patients with dementia. The misdiagnosis leads to the patient being prescribed yet again another brain drug for a disease they don't even have.

As always, anecdotal information and the experiences of patients are as important to me as studying the available science. For this I went to online groups for benzodiazepines. I was curious to see if other people had also experienced seizures. Unexpectedly, I found people describing symptoms that were very similar to some of Pat's troubling behaviour that she had developed in the last few years. One stood out in particular. A lady responded to one of my comments saying during her withdrawal she wore out several pairs of shoes with all the pacing back and forth she did. I was instantly transported back in time and remembered coming home only to find Pat pacing back and forth through the house in a high state of agitation. I asked her why she was doing this and she said didn't know why. She felt compelled to pace and was frustrated not knowing what was driving this behaviour.

Many of the people in the benzodiazepine groups were also on other brain drugs, so this prompted me to do a review of Pat's chart. I found Pat had been on nine different brain drugs going as far back as 1998. Now my research expanded to include the effects of all these drugs. All of them altered the function of the brain's neurotransmitters and shared many of the same side effects. Side effects that many in the online groups were describing and many of the side effects also were descriptions for Pat's behavioural issues: anxiety, depression, mood swings, memory loss and difficulty thinking to name a few. Some of the drugs Pat was taking were not considered addictive, but all had the potential for abuse. That is contradictory double speak that is common with pharmaceutical companies. All of these drugs modify the function of specific neurotransmitters and their respective receptor sites. There are too many unknowns about how these drugs work to make any claims about how they affect the brain let alone if they are addictive or not. Besides, I found out that regulatory agencies approve drugs based on summary tables provided to them by the pharmaceutical manufacturers and are not given access to the raw data from the randomized clinical trials. So there is no way to verify if any of the claims made by the pharmaceutical manufacturers are true.

The online groups also introduced me to the theory of protracted withdrawal syndrome. This was attributed to people who tapered off a drug too quickly or abruptly stopped taking the drug altogether. The theory of tapering off a brain drug is to give the neurotransmitter receptor sites a chance to heal and hopefully restore their proper function. Pat had never properly tapered off any of the drugs she had taken over those years. Could the troubling behaviour that Pat had developed be the result of protracted withdrawal syndrome? A question that could probably never be really answered now, but it was reasonable to think that they could have been a contributor to her problems.

Now I'll segue back to my original line of query: did the lorazepam drug cause Pat's seizure? Over the years, Pat had been prescribed Wellbutrin, Zoloft, Neurontin, Celexa, Prozac, Exelon and most recently lorazepam. All listed seizures as "incidence not known". This means that seizures were acknowledged to have happened, but a count was not tabulated because there were too few reports of its occurrence. Remember, this information is provided by pharmaceutical manufacturers that do not allow access to raw data. Regardless, seizures are not something to be dismissed just because there were few reported cases. If these drugs can trigger a seizure it needs to be known. This is also a failure of the regulatory agencies whose mandate is protect public health. Besides, this does not reconcile the claim that seizures are rare and then warn tapering off the drug may trigger seizures. Here's what I know: Pat never had a seizure in her life before taking lorazepam and there was no family history of seizures. My conclusion was that, until I found out anything that could lead me to think differently, her seizure was caused by the drug. I would be lying to say that I felt comfortable with this, but I had no choice. Seeing is believing under these conditions.

While I was reading the literature on these drugs, I was introduced to another term I hadn't heard before: tardive dyskinesia. This is a disorder that causes involuntary movements of the face, mouth and tongue. The documentation for the benzodiazepine that Pat was taking said that females between fifty and fifty-nine years old were a risk group for developing TD from Lorazepam. This side effect can happen even if it is only taken for a month or less. In the few weeks that she had been taking lorazepam, Pat's face would contort in way that's difficult to describe. It sort of looked like her face was having a mini earthquake and her face was a mask that about to fall off. I spent time in front of a mirror trying to mimic the movement, but couldn't even come close. One source I read suggested that benzodiazepines may be a useful in treating antipsychotic drug-induced TD while another source stated that benzodiazepines may cause TD. Medicine is riddled with conflicting views like this and it makes it very difficult to do your due diligence.

Over the next few months after the initial seizure, a more serious condition arose. I could be standing nose to nose with Pat and she would fold up at the waist like a jack knife and hit the floor hard before I had any chance to react. I did find a condition called atonic seizures that described the same thing. Atonic seizures are said to happen when there is an electrical surge in the brain. Atonic seizures (also known as drop seizures) cause a sudden loss of muscle strength resulting in a fall, all while the patient remains fully conscious. This was the case for Pat because immediately after having the drop seizure, she was trying to get back to her feet. Weird. I didn't find lorazepam having this as a side effect, but it was a side effect for selective serotonin reuptake inhibitors (SSRI). SSRIs were a class of drug she had been prescribed in the past. SSRIs has been approved for use, but the documentation acknowledges that it is not known how this drug actually works. How can a drug be approved for the market without knowing how it actually works? To add to the confusion, the term selective serotonin reuptake inhibitor is neither a scientific nor a medical term, but a marketing term from a major pharmaceutical manufacturer.

This is a mess. There appears to be no cost/benefit analysis conducted for the approval of drugs or medical devices. The "big picture" seems to be absent in clinical practice as well. A prime example of this is poly-drugging. Even though patients are asked to bring a list of their prescriptions, there is little consideration of drug interaction between prescriptions. Poly-drugging injures or kills thousands of patients every year. Some studies suggest that "brain drugs" may also compromise the immune system. Suppression of the immune system inhibits the body's ability to fight off attack. Conversely, chronically attacking the body with a damaging drug can trigger an autoimmune response. Proper immune function is critical for a body to be able to defend itself. Medicine that doesn't even consider that it may be harming the body's own ability to defend itself is bad medicine. MEDICAL COMMUNITY, what the hell are you thinking?

The recent discovery of neuroplasticity has rendered compartmentalizing the brain inaccurate. Neuroplasticity is the ability of the brain to completely rewire itself if part of it gets injured through trauma or disease. If the area for speech gets damaged, then neuroplastic therapy can retrain a different area of the brain for speech. Mainstream medicine knows this, but hasn't even scratched the surface for its therapeutic benefits. What kind of neuroplastic effects do benzodiazepines have on the brain in the short term? Or for the long term? This is a fair and very important question to consider. I think it's important to point out that any "neuroplasticians" that I have read about do not use brain drugs in treating their patients. If the brain were a compartmentalized organ, then the use of drugs might make sense, but neuroplasticity shows that the brain cannot be thought of this way or treated this way.

SETTLING IN, GETTING DOWN TO BUSINESS

You need to learn how to slow down
and take life in stride
Just take it easy
we're just along for the ride

Sometimes in life an opportunity presents itself and the decision to proceed doesn't require debate or thinking it over. It's right and you know it. That's how we felt about the area that we found ourselves in and we decided to rent for a year before deciding whether we wanted to buy a home. During the year it only became clearer that this was a great place to settle down. I didn't think I would ever find a place in Canada that I wanted to live. The following year we made our decision to buy a home. A nice modest little home with a detached garage on a huge fenced-in lot. Our new home was on a dead end street and two blocks from a private beachside park that the neighbourhood shared. Most importantly Pat would be safe here.

Our little town was the southernmost point in Canada on the shores of beautiful Lake Erie and surrounded by farm land. Windsor, with a metro population of about 350k, was a half hour away and right across the river was Detroit Michigan. We like visiting the US and this area was unique in that there was a major US city right next door. Everywhere else in Canada requires several hours of driving to get to a major US city. Detroit was experiencing a renewal after several years of decline. Music is a passion for me and Detroit has a rich music culture. The city has its own music genre…MOTOWN! I didn't know it right away, but this little village was also home to several veteran and active professional musicians. The village also a robust visual arts community. The area had several wine-producing vineyards and where there's wine, there usually is food. Although the town proper had about 15k people, there were several eateries and the town was becoming a destination for foodies. Lake Erie was a reasonable facsimile to replace the saltwater that we grew up with in Atlantic Canada.

The stability of a home base would help a lot for Pat's sense of well being and mine too. We found Pat a primary doctor with the intention of restarting her quarterly blood tests for iron and semi-annual liver imaging to make sure her liver was not deteriorating. The next order of business was to find a functional medicine doctor. The functional medicine approach is holistic and systems-oriented. It endeavours to treat causes rather than treating symptoms. It is also a more collaborative effort between patient and practitioner and individualized in that it considers a patient's genetics, biochemistry and lifestyle. Treating human biology as a system is a more realistic view than treating the body as a collection of component parts. Another benefit of a systems approach is the greater likelihood of identifying more than one underlying cause for an observed symptom. Addressing the root causes and treating them is better medicine and increases the chance for a more successful outcome. Conversely, a root cause could be a problem for more than one health issue. Treating the human body holistically is obvious to me and doesn't require a medical degree to understand this. It's just common sense. The one pill/one treatment paradigm of mainstream medicine has a long history of failure and many times exacerbates a health problem. The one pill/one treatment paradigm serves the industrial side of the medical/industrial complex because it only has to justify the product it's selling with no consideration of possible problems it may be causing to the enclosed biological system we call the human body.

At our first appointment with Pat's new primary care physician, I brought up Pat's seizure and if lorazepam could have been the cause. He said that was only in rare cases. I asked him how did he know she wasn't a rare case? Can a test be administered to see if she is a rare case? He said there was no such test. As I kept pressing, he got more and more agitated. Why was he getting agitated by my questions? I was just trying to get answers and understand what happened. Then it dawned on me what was happening. He was repeating talking points that were handed down to him. He had no direct knowledge one way or the other if lorazepam had caused the seizure. I didn't think of it at the time, but my questions were essentially calling him out. He was getting frustrated because he knew he had no explanation. I knew he didn't know because Pat did the same thing with her patients. Information she had about the drugs she prescribed to her patients was hand-me-down info and not based on any clinical experience from her own practice. I also knew that doctors would have a very difficult time questioning themselves if their treatments were a contributing to their patient's health problems. To be fair, doctors should be able to trust the information provided by the regulatory agencies for safe and effective treatments for their patients. However, they have many patients and I have only one, Pat. When medicine wasn't solving her health questions, I started asking questions about the effectiveness of the medicine provided to her. Doctors have hundreds of patients with unresolved health issues and just go along with the status quo, ignoring the shortcomings of the system and avoiding the serious soul searching that they must face. That is until it happens to you personally like it did us. To question the bubble/paradigm you first have to admit you're in a bubble. Along our journey we found other doctors and nurses who had stepped away from mainstream medicine This wouldn't be the last time that a doctor would get frustrated with me for asking questions. I would never forget this lesson and would recognize the repetition of talking points going forward. We needed real answers, not talking points.

Next I went online to find a functional medicine practitioner. The body is capable of self-repair and you don't need a medical degree to know this. Functional medicine isn't the only medical approach that treats human health from a holistic point of view. The functional medicine approach to me was a combination of western medicine with complementary/alternative medicine. We wanted to find a medical doctor that used this complementary approach in their practice and who would still have full access to the regular medical system and its resources. Functional medicine certification is also a recognized CME (continuing medical education) credit. We found an anesthesiologist in private practice who incorporated functional medicine in his practice to treat his patients. When we contacted him for an appointment, he told us if we got a referral from Pat's primary care doctor the initial consult would be covered by the Canadian single-payer health insurance. After that, costs would be out of our pocket. This doctor's training and certifications were impressive, but what intrigued me the most was that he came to functional medicine to find a way for dealing with pain management within his own family. This was another doctor who looked outside the system to resolve personal health issues. This meant he was open-minded and not constricted to a paradigm. The original motivation to resolve a health issue within his own family also meant that he would have thoroughly investigated the merits of this approach to medical care. He had extensive training in alternative medical approaches in addition to having a medical degree in mainstream medicine.

Holistic medicine is a more comprehensive approach. Making adjustments in a person's lifestyle and diet promotes good health and in some cases removes the source of a health problem. It has been said, "our genes load the gun but the environment pulls the trigger". Exposure to environmental toxins is real and it is not something that should be dismissed. The functional med doctor explained his strategy on how he was going to treat Pat and answered our questions about the treatments he was going to use. He followed this up at each appointment by providing us with information specific for what he was doing that day. He gave us handouts and websites for the products he was using and the same for his treatments. We really appreciated this compared to being kept in the dark concerning her health care thus far. His openness gave me confidence in his abilities and I was able to let my guard down, feeling comfortable in passing off Pat's health care to him. We brought along the results of the heavy metal test that had been done the year before. He said the lab that we sent the urine sample to in Alberta didn't actually do the lab work. They were an intermediary and the lab analysis was done in Chicago. He knew the lab in Chicago and didn't question the accuracy of their work, but the intermediary was an unnecessary cost to us. This is when I realized that a good doctor not only has sound clinical practices but also knew where to get things done and had thoroughly vetted the products he was using to treat his patients. After the initial improvement after removing the mercury fillings and the chelation program, Pat's demeanour was starting to backslide and I was hoping that we could get this back on track working with this new doctor.

An intake questionnaire arrived in the mail and we were to fill it out prior to our first appointment. It was twenty-eight pages long including a week's worth of the meals Pat ate to determine if any adjustments should be made to her diet. In addition to the intake questionnaire, we filled out a symptoms questionnaire when we arrived for each appointment to help measure progress. The symptoms questionnaire had fifteen different categories with several questions for each. It used a rating system from 0 through to 4; 0 was never or almost never and at the other end 4 indicated frequent or severe symptoms. Mainstream medicine disregards anecdotal information and experiences and believes that the answer to lack of science is more science. This is by definition a bubble and an elitist top-down point of view. Patient feedback is important no matter how subjective or objective it is. It also gives the patient a chance to participate in their care, forming an important collaboration between doctor and patient. As the patient thinks for themselves, their responses can get fine-tuned providing more and more accurate information for the attending physician to act upon.

His first line of investigation was to test Pat for autonomic dysfunction. This was timely because this issue had been brought to my attention recently in a conversation with Pat's cousin. She was also a doctor and a sufferer of Crohn's disease. She had a lot of empathy for Pat's gastrointestinal problem. The human body has two nervous systems: the somatic and autonomic. The somatic system is under our voluntary control. The autonomic system works in the background controlling and regulating bodily functions like heart rate, digestion and respiratory rate among other things. Pat had to walk around a lot to get her gut moving so it seemed reasonable to me this may be an indication of autonomic dysfunction. The diagnostic method he used was autonomic response testing or neural kinesiology. I had heard of kinesiology in relation to sports, but didn't know much about it. In Canada, kinesiology has a regulated professional designation and practitioners work in the health care alongside physio and occupational therapists. They also help patients with work-related injuries and car accident victims and do functional assessments for patient progress. Autonomic response testing is a blend of American kinesiology, German bio-feedback and European neural therapy. It also considers an individual's psychology, neurological issues and biochemistry. The theory was that the ailment interrupts the natural flow of energy through the body and that the blockages can be isolated and corrected using elements of kinesiology and neural therapy. Bizarre. Weird. Not so fast. The body has electrical currents running through it and electrical currents have polarities. Disturbances in the electrical fields in the body can affect the homeostasis that the body desires. I had no problem with the idea of working with the body's energy fields for diagnosing or possible treatments involving electrical currents within the body. Mainstream medicine used electroencephalograms to measure electrical signals in the brain to help diagnose brain disorders. Mainstream medicine also had adopted acupuncture, which uses the energy fields in the Bonghan lines to alleviate the effects of chemo in treating cancers. An example of the importance of electrical charges in the body can be understood with free radicals. Free radicals are electrons or molecules with a net positive or negative electrical charge looking for a place to bind. Some of these free radicals the body recombines in ways useful for the body. Other free radicals are disposed of by the body's own antioxidant abilities. However, some are not eliminated and these roaming free radicals have been implicated in causing harm to proteins, lipids and even DNA. I decided to go online and do some cross referencing to see what mainstream medicine had to say about the autonomic nervous system.

Up until now there had never been any autonomic dysfunction investigations ordered for Pat and not once was it even mentioned. I quickly found that mainstream medicine acknowledged that heavy metal toxicity could contribute to autonomic dysfunction. Standard testing for autonomic nerve damage included blood tests, spinal fluid tests, CT and MRI scans, and electromyography (nerve conduction studies). Interestingly, mainstream medicine also includes muscle strength tests (kinesiology) for autonomic dysfunction. Mainstream medicine's position is that autonomic dysfunction cannot be cured, but it can be prevented or managed if a patent suffers from it. Management plans included treating other underlying gut issues first to eliminate that variable. Since there was no direct way to treat autonomic gastrointestinal problems, diet plans for good gut function were put in place. Increasing dietary fibre, drinking plenty of fluids, prescription drugs that increase the contractions of the digestive tract, laxatives for constipation and a round of antibiotics to reduce unwanted bacterial growth. We had already gotten a heads-up from Pat's cousin who had Crohn's disease about using laxatives. Laxatives should only be used sparingly or else the gut will develop a dependency and get lazy in doing its job. Prescribing antibiotics may be useful in the short term, but correcting imbalances in gut bacteria and enzymes were a much better option to restore balance in the gut. If a patient was experiencing pain, over-the-counter pain relievers were recommended or pain medications were prescribed. Pain medications were a double-edged sword because most of them can cause constipation. Other considerations for gut dysfunction were correcting vitamin deficiencies, losing weight, avoiding toxins, and regular exercise. Whether Pat had autonomic dysfunction or not, it made perfect sense to restore proper gut function by eliminating toxins and bad bacteria with good bacteria and enzymes.

The functional med doctor determined that Pat had low ATP (adenosine triphosphate). ATP is an organic compound which is used by the mitochondria for generating energy. Getting the mitochondria functioning properly and running like a well-oiled machine was one of the first steps that the doctor took. He thought it was likely that the heavy metal overload was causing mitochondrial stress. I found this interesting. I remembered learning about the role of the mitochondria from a college biology course. I found it fascinating and understood the fundamental role it played in human biology and the importance of good mitochondrial health. The mitochondria are organelles found in most cells. Their primary job is generating energy, but they also store calcium, generate heat and mediate cell growth and cell death. Mitochondria play a very fundamental role in human biology and there is evidence that mitochondrial dysfunction is a contributor to chronic and degenerative diseases. He started Pat on a supplement called Mito-Matrix. The supplement contained four ingredients to bolster mitochondrial function. Acetyl-L-Carnitine can improve cognition, mood and maybe most importantly for Pat ALC protects nerve function which could have been damaged by "brain" drugs she had taken. N-accetyl cysteine is an amino acid needed to build glutathione, which is our body's master antioxidant. NAC is used to help protect the liver, which would be good for Pat's damaged liver. Alpha-lipoic acid, in addition to improving mitochondria, helps to regulate blood sugars, protects the nervous system and chelates heavy metals such as mercury. Coenzyme Q10 is a powerful antioxidant and is necessary for cellular energy production.

The doctor started Pat on a detoxification program for detoxing organ tissue and improved circulation to help clear out the toxins from the body. Specifically the detox program targeted the liver, gallbladder, intestines, kidney and lymphatic system. I think people are regularly exposed to toxins from several sources and a regular detoxification program should be a part of everyone's preventative health care particularly for those with chronic health problems. Toxicities can build up for years before symptoms appear and many times those symptoms are wrongly diagnosed, leading to unnecessary treatments which could lead to health problems in itself. There were three detoxification supplements that worked together using a combination of herbs and homeopathy. A-hepatica is an herbal combination for detoxification of the liver and gallbladder. German physicians had been using this formula for many decades as a liver detoxifier. It regulates secretion and absorption in the digestive system, has anti-inflammatory properties, and stimulates bile flow. Lymf-A-Drop, the second supplement, helps the body's elimination organs and supports the liver, biliary tract, skin, lungs, and gastrointestinal tract. It also helps to detoxify the blood and drain toxins stored in the extracellular and connective tissues. The homeopathic formula was for the bladder, urinary tract and kidneys. Urinating was never a problem for Pat.

After the round of detoxification was complete, he started Pat on a chelation program. For this he used a product that had chlorella pyrenoidosa as the active ingredient. He preferred a slower chelation approach because too rapid a chelation can cause toxic reactions. Chlorella has been used in the removal of radioactive particles from the body after radiation treatment for cancer. Chlorella is a freshwater algae and has the highest amount of chlorophyll of any known plant. In addition to acting as a chelating agent to remove heavy metals it may boost the immune system and help fight infection. Another bonus for Pat was that it increases the good bacteria in the gastrointestinal tract. It could be considered a super food because it contains 60 percent protein, eighteen amino acids (including all the essential amino acids) and several vitamins and minerals. Japanese researchers found that chlorella may have anti-tumour properties that help fight against breast cancer. Through researching Pat's health problems I gained a lot of respect for the Japanese, German and Israeli health systems. Over the next few months, the functional med doctor had Pat do two more rounds of supplements to restore her gut biome, after which she was put a permanent supplement program to maintain her gastrointestinal tract.

The new doctor also diagnosed Pat with leaky gut syndrome. This is yet another controversial diagnosis that has supporters and detractors. Differences of opinion between doctors create a healthy debate that helps focus and fine-tune medical investigations. That's in a perfect world, but differences of opinion can be distorted by misinformation, self-serving business interests and egotistical turf wars jockeying for who gets the funding dollars. Leaky gut is a term that will not be mentioned in medical schools very much even though it is mainstream medicine that first diagnosed it and has over four hundred peer-reviewed papers on the subject. However, medical students will hear the term selective serotonin reuptake inhibitor even though it isn't a scientific or medical term, but a term from the marketing department of a major pharmaceutical company. Irritable bowel syndrome is another diagnosis from mainstream medicine although they admit the cause isn't precisely known. Leaky gut syndrome, intestinal permeability and irritable bowel syndrome all share common symptoms: abdominal pain, cramping, bloating, excess gas, diarrhea and constipation. In addition to sorting out terminology, the discerning patient is faced with a medical system that says there is much about the gut that is unknown as a whole. Our intestinal tract is our biggest immune system organ, so why is there not much known about the gut's role in protecting the human body? This points out a fundamental flaw in mainstream medicine's paradigm of care. The human body has tremendous ability to take care of itself. There is a broad spectrum of examples of the body's ability for self-repair from people surviving inexplicable death-defying odds to simple paper cuts healing all by themselves. From this point of view, medicine cures nothing by itself and in reality assists the body in self-repair. It should be a fundamental priority for the medical system to understand the human body's immune system to support and assist it if necessary, not ignore it.

The intestinal lining has over 4000 square feet of surface area that controls what enters the blood stream. The idea behind leaky gut (or intestinal permeability) is the surface area becomes too permeable, allowing partially digested food, toxins, and other unwanted substance into the blood stream. Undigested food particles, bacterial toxins and germs that pass through the intestinal wall trigger an immune system response creating inflammation. Chronic assault can result in an autoimmune dysfunction like Crohn's disease. Some studies also attribute leaky gut to lupus, type 1 diabetes, multiple sclerosis, arthritis and even mental illness. A diet free of processed foods high in sugar and low in fibre is replaced by a diet of unprocessed foods which includes food free from pesticides and other possible toxins as much as possible. Again this is common sense and it was part of the strategy that the functional medicine doctor was going to use in treating Pat.

The functional med doctor treated Pat with ultraviolet blood irradiation (UBI) over the course of three sessions. Great. What is UBI? The doctor supplied us with a generous amount of reading material and dozens of web links so we could read up on the subject. Ultraviolet radiation is used to purify water of micro-organisms, decontaminate surgical equipment and kill viruses and bacteria on surfaces including human skin. There are hundreds of published and peer-reviewed papers on the use and effectiveness for using UBI. The US FDA approved its use in treating T-cell lymphoma and there are clinical trials that look promising for treating immune diseases like multiple sclerosis, rheumatoid arthritis and lupus. UBI was a part of mainstream medicine from 1930 to 1965, but was sidelined by the rise of antibiotics. There is a resurgence in the use of UBI driven by super bugs that are impervious to current antibiotics. The procedure the functional med doctor used in his treatment for Pat was drawing about 250 cc of blood, exposing the blood sample to UV light and returning it to the patient intravenously. The UV light deactivates the viruses and bacteria by penetrating the cell walls. Then the body's own clean-up crew, macrophages, engulfs the garbage and clears it from the body. The recorded experiences for UBI reported virtually no side effects so there was no reason not to try this therapy. We would determine its worthiness by our most important metric, results.

So what did we accomplish by seeing the functional medicine doctor? After years of Pat's gut being locked up with constipation, this treatment made a tremendous improvement providing much needed relief for her. This in turn relieved the associated stress and anxiety that went with it. Although her gut improved, her "drop seizures" were getting worse and more dangerous. Her speech problems continued to deteriorate as well. However, the gains from his treatments were going to be derailed by an unfortunate event. I learned of a term through the investment world called a black swan event. A black swan is an unexpected event that comes out of nowhere and completely changes the trajectory you are on. Pat's black swan would cause a setback that she would never be able to recover from. A real deal breaker.

OUT OF THE BLUE

There is also an immense sadness.
It completely engulfs me and there is no mercy in it

Whether Pat was experiencing gut pain or anxiety, she found that going for walks helped a lot. We were fortunate to live one block away from a beautiful lakeside park, an oasis right on the shores of Lake Erie. We walked it several times a day. The park was established in 1907 and received heritage status on its centennial in 2007. It is beloved and a well-used amenity in the community. Its natural amphitheatre is the location of a successful annual folk festival that runs on a mid-August weekend. It has its walking paths and a playground frequented by young families. A volunteer horticultural society maintains its gardens. A beautiful cobblestone bridge built in 1928 spans the stream running through the park. The pavilion seems to be almost in continuous use, hosting many wedding receptions, but also events like the annual art and crafts festival. The local schools have sporting events in the spring and fall, but my favourite is the annual Fantasy of Lights Festival held during the Christmas season. Wire frames shaped in seasonal images of candy canes, candles and snowmen are all lit up with Christmas lights. All the wire frames were built by students in the town's schools. We were fortunate to have such a resource one block away from where we lived.

On one of our walks through the park, we met a young lady

walking a dog. The little fella ran up wagging his tail and was really eager to meet our acquaintance. She said that she was taking care of him until someone would give him a forever home. This was fortuitous. Pat and I are dog lovers and we wanted to have a dog in our lives again. We were interested in big dogs and this little guy was a mix of West Highland Terrier and Maltese. Although he was a pint-sized pup, he had a full-size bark. We brought him home and after a week we decided to keep him. A Westie came from the same part of Scotland that Pat's family came from. Bossy little bugger, he thinks he's the sheriff of the neighbourhood.

One morning we were on our way for our walk in the park and, while turning the corner at the end of the block, Pat stumbled and fell. When I got her up on her feet she howled in pain. She couldn't put weight on her left leg. This was the leg that had had a hip replacement in 2006. A gentleman driving by saw that we were in trouble and stopped his car to offer help. He took our rambunctious puppy's leash and walked with us back to our door. I got Pat back in the house, but she couldn't even find a comfortable way to sit without being in pain. I didn't know the extent of the injury and, instead of trying to get her into the car, I called an ambulance. Images were taken in the emergency room and they found that the thigh bone where the post from the prosthetic extended down had hair line cracks. She was admitted to hospital. The next morning she was ambulated from the small local hospital to be examined by an orthopedic surgeon at a larger regional hospital in Windsor. I followed in my car. When the ambulance arrived at the hospital, Pat was taken to an examining room. It wasn't long before the orthopedic surgeon arrived. He didn't enter the examining room and just leaned against the door with his arms crossed. He asked a few questions of the nurse that accompanied Pat and didn't come into the room to do a physical examination. I didn't expect this, but I shouldn't have been surprised because I know how the system works. The images taken and reports could have simply been sent to him, but the orthopedic surgeon needed to be in the patient's presence to be officially part of her care to get paid. He got paid for doing absolutely nothing. The appointment was short and Pat was ambulated back to the admitting hospital. I made arrangements for a hospital bed, walker, a raised commode to be brought to our home and in-home visits for personal care givers, including an occupational therapist. Several weeks passed by and Pat wasn't really making any progress and then, out of the blue, disaster struck.

Pat hadn't a grand mal seizure in months until early one morning around 2am. Pat's seizures typically started by her body going rigid, then going limp and, when she starts coming around, she would be very agitated and would want to get up and pace. I couldn't let her up and pace with her injured hip. After several minutes of trying to calm her down, she was only getting more agitated so I called the ambulance. I arrived at the emergency room about a half hour later. Pat was laying on a mat on the floor covered by a blanket and whimpering. They sedated her to calm her down. I explained to the emergency room doctor what had happened and her injured hip. He surprised me by saying that I could take her home. I asked him how he expected me to take her home sedated like that and how I could safely manipulate her hip to get her in the car. His attitude was indifference. It was in the middle of the night and I had to wait a few hours for a private ambulatory service to be available to bring her home. When she was brought home, she was placed in the hospital bed that we had in the living room. Pat slept all that day and through the night. The following morning I threw back the blankets covering Pat and had the shock of my life. Her left leg with the injured hip was about three inches shorter than her right leg and her foot was pointing at the wall instead of the ceiling. The seizure had resulted in completely breaking the hip! This was obvious just by looking at it, no X-ray necessary. I called the ambulance again. One of the technicians was about my age and he was shocked as well. He decided that he was going to ambulate Pat to a much larger hospital in Chatham,

Ontario, and, as he put it, "I'm going to get into deep shit for this, but I'm not taking her back to the hospital where I work."

We had been frustrated by the medical community's insistence that Pat had Alzheimer's disease despite it having been overturned by leading health professionals from within their own community. Up until now this was preventing serious investigations about Pat's health issues, but now their insistence had become dangerous. The emergency room assumed that Pat's agitation was dementia-related when in reality she was suffering pain from the largest joint in the body being broken. Obviously, the emergency room doctor didn't even throw back the blanket or else he would have seen that her hip was broken. This is a disgrace. What if a blood clot happened or some other serious complication that might have cost Pat her life? I understand how disgraceful this was more than many other people reading this would. Pat did emergency room shifts for years and sometimes she would see patients from her practice coming through. A doctor cannot make assumptions about patients who come through an emergency no matter how well they know them. Wrong assumptions could lead to something serious being overlooked. To drive this point home, we have other doctors in the family who have done emergency rooms shifts who also know this. The emergency room doctor that saw Pat should have been reprimanded for doing that, if not fired.

The hospital in Chatham was about an hour away and the ambulance driver suggested that I stay home and call the hospital later in the evening. He said it would take some time to find a bed for Pat and be admitted. I called later that evening and the nurse asked me a few questions about what had happened and questions regarding Pat's health history. I drove up that same evening and Pat was still in the emergency department, but resting quietly. She was doing fine so I drove back home. Around 11:30pm the hospital gave me a call and said that, due to the extent of the injury, Pat was going to be ambulated to a hospital in London, Ontario. After their orthopedic surgeons reviewed the imaging, they thought it was best to send her London Health Science, where their orthopedic surgical team had more experience in dealing with complicated injuries. Pat's hip was mangled pretty bad. I drove up to London early in the afternoon the next day. It was a two-hour drive and I would make that drive every day for the next five days. I met one of the doctors from the orthopedic team to explain what happened and Pat's health history. They told me that a revision would be required to repair Pat's hip. It was a bit more complicated than usual because of some soft tissue injury around the hip. (My dear reader, try to remember this soft tissue "injury" because soft tissue surrounding the hips is going to come up again later on in this chapter.) The problem was with the post that extended into the femur. The receiving end cup in the pelvic bone was fine and undamaged. The revision surgery would have to be delayed for a few days because a new custom-made replacement post would have to be made. The orthopedic surgeon said that the original post was only a couple of inches long and was a bad choice to begin with. The new post was three times as long and should be a lot more stable. This sounded logical to me. It took three days to get the replacement parts and when it arrived the surgery was scheduled for the next day.

I was travelling to London every day and I brought along smoothies that had the gut supplements that she had been taking. Despite this effort, all the progress that the functional medicine doctor achieved in improving Pat's gut function was wiped out. Pat was placed on several pain medications and every drug caused constipation. Pat was experiencing a locked-up gut again and the severe pain that went with it. I have never had gut problems, but a few weeks later I got first-hand experience of the suffering that Pat was going through with her gut. Pat was given a prescription for pain medications after she was released to go home. I avoided giving them to her as much as possible because I wanted to get her gut back to the base line we had established. I occasionally get really bad headaches and I thought I would try one of her pain medications. The next morning I had constipation so bad that it felt like I was trying to pass a brick. This is when I realized what Pat had been going through for several years now. No wonder she was severely agitated and wanted to go for walks when she was having constipation. Empathy is difficult unless you walk a mile in that person's shoes.

Pat needed to get up and walk around to get her gut moving, but it was too soon after her hip surgery to be able to do it herself. Once again she was in severe pain, which the nursing staff thought was due to Alzheimer's disease. They weren't buying my explanation that she was suffering from severe constipation and she needed to get up and move around to get her gut moving. I assured them that I had seen this many times and, after a successful bathroom trip, Pat's agitation would settle down. I also told them that it may take several bathroom visits before the mission was accomplished. The care givers told Pat to just poop in the bed and they will come and help clean her up after. This wasn't going to work because she needed to move in order for her gut to move. London Health Sciences was one of Canada's leading hospitals and they didn't have enough staff to help a patient with the bathroom? Instead of helping to avoid the indignity of crapping in her underwear, their solution was to give her more pain medications and Seroquel to settle the agitation. Seroquel is an antipsychotic medication! Doping a patient into submission with an antipsychotic may have made the staff's life easier, but that is disgraceful care coming from a leading hospital. I pressed to have Pat ambulated back to the hospital in Leamington for the rest of her convalescence. This was the same hospital that sent her home with the broken hip in the first place, but it was minutes from home instead of the one-way two-hour drive to London. I could be by her side much more often and keep an eye on how she was being treated. I was reluctant to bring her home too quickly, fearing she may have another seizure. I couldn't be certain that I may have contributed to the breaking of her hip by trying to prevent her from getting out of bed that night. It was a damned if you do and damned if you don't situation, but it would have to do for now.

Pat had lost faith in the medical system some time ago and now due to this whole hip fiasco she was now really scared of hospitals. She hated being in the hospital. She was still being given pain medications that were ruining her gut and she was still being given brain medications to mitigate her "agitation". Hospitalists are in-house doctors that take care of inpatients. I talked to the young hospitalist about the brain medications. She said finding the right brain medications and successful dosages was done by trial and error. Trial and error again. You're giving someone a brain medication when all they need is have a good shit. I tried to get Pat to exercise a bit to get her hip working again and be able to stand and walk steady. I wanted to get her out of there as fast as I could. She was provided a walker to help with this. Pat would grab the walker, but it never touched the floor. She was almost sprinting up and down the hall trying to find an exit to get out. The nurses at the nursing station were watching in disbelief because she after all just had hip surgery. She stayed at the hospital for six days and I got her the hell out of there and took her home. It took several months to get her gut working properly again. In-home care was provided, personal care workers and some physio, but it was superficial and worthless. This was a very trying experience. Over the next few months, we were able to get her gut back to the base line that was established prior to the hip fracture.

One evening I stumbled upon a documentary on Netflix called *The Bleeding Edge*. The documentary was about the medical device industry. The medical device industry is far larger than the pharmaceutical industry in terms of revenue and therefore has far more lobbying power. I had no idea. The medical device industry is one of the fastest growing industries and is growing faster than the regulatory agencies' ability to properly assess their products for public safety and effectiveness. The documentary covered several medical devices, but what really caught my attention was a segment on hip prosthetics for artificial hip replacements. An orthopedic surgeon was interviewed who had trouble with his own hip replacement. At first the prosthetic worked fine, but he started to notice he was having cognitive problems. He was repeating himself a lot, developed tinnitus and had tremors in his hands. The problems were getting worse and came to a head eighteen months after his hip replacement. While he was attending a medical conference, he had a complete mental break down. He trashed the hotel room he was staying in and wrote all over the walls and ceiling with a black felt tip marker. He didn't explain the details the subsequent investigations to find the cause, but at some point he decided to check for his cobalt levels and found the levels were 100 times higher than they should be. The hip prosthetic used for his hip replacement was a metal-on-metal cobalt/chromium alloy. He decided to undergo surgery to replace the cobalt/chromium hip with a plastic socket and a ceramic femoral head. Gradually his cognitive issues were resolved as the cobalt levels dropped. Then he said something I'll never forget, "I wouldn't have believed a cobalt hip prosthetic could ever have caused these problems if it hadn't happened to me." WOW! I immediately looked in Pat's chart and the hip replacement she had done in 2006 was cobalt/chromium. The hip revision that was done just a few months ago was also a cobalt/chromium. Looking back, Pat started developing cognitive issues about eighteen months after she had the hip replacement back in 2006. Eleven years after her initial hip surgery, a few months after her hip revision, years of investigations that went nowhere and the thousands of hours I spent researching (groping, really) on my own to unravel Pat's health issues, I was just now finding out about cobalt poisoning from a hip replacement. I have no doubt that hemochromatosis and brain drugs were contributors to Pat's health issues, but cobalt poisoning was the best fit to the timeline for when Pat started developing symptoms. Now what?

The orthopedic surgeon in the documentary described his hip revision to replace the cobalt metal-on-metal prosthetic. The ligaments and soft tissue surrounding his hip joint had liquefied. (This is why I wanted you to remember above that the surgeons saw Pat had soft tissue injury around her hip. What did they see soft tissue injury from a broken hip or tissue that was injured from years of cobalt poisoning? Hold this thought because more is coming below.) Also when they opened up the orthopedic surgeon's hip for the replacement, the metal socket looked like dirty engine oil with metal fragments! Luckily once the poisonous cobalt was removed, the surgeon's cognitive issues were resolved and he was able to go back to living his normal life.

This experience prompted the surgeon to contact the manufacturers of the metal-on-metal cobalt hip prosthetic to see if there were any other reported cases. They said no. The Centers for Disease Control and the Food and Drug Administration hadn't issued any alerts either. He didn't stop there and started paying attention to the cognitive complaints from his own patients and tested their cobalt levels. He found many had elevated cobalt levels and those who had the MOM cobalt hip replaced had their cognitive disorders resolved. Some of his patients who were experiencing cognitive disorders were wrongly diagnosed with Alzheimer's disease and subjected to drugs that only worsened their condition. Working hand in hand with a diagnostic radiologist, they also found the brain damage from cobalt poisoning had the same characteristics as an Alzheimer's brain. Reluctantly, he essentially conducted a study on the harms of cobalt poisoning with the patients he had in his own practice. He felt moral obligation to do so and expressed frustration for doing the work that was the responsibility of CDC and FDA. On average he found that 25 percent of his cobalt hip patients suffered no symptoms and 25 percent of his patients suffered debilitating cognitive disorders. The middle 50 percent suffered milder forms of cognitive disability. How could this have happened if the products from the medical industry have to meet rigorous testing and lengthy pre-market approval standards? One reason is the 510(k) loophole. If a hip prosthetic was substantially equivalent to a previous generation of prosthetic, the product could bypass pre-market approval rules. If the original predicate hip prosthetic eventually was found to be unsafe, it was taken off the market, but the "new and improved" products continued to be used. That's the regulatory agencies who are supposed to look out for you my friends.

After watching this documentary, I went online to find more information about poisoning from cobalt hip replacements. There was quite a bit of information to be found and the experiences of patients who were affected, but an orthopedic surgeon from the United Kingdom stood out in particular. He characterized the problems that some of his hip replacement patients were having as an "invisible pathology." Some of his patients had started out fine, but in time problems developed. Complaints of groin pain and having trouble lifting the leg that had received the hip implant. He withdrew some fluid from the hip joint and found what looked like pus, but laboratory results did not indicate an infection. Investigative surgery found that muscle and other soft tissue around the hip was either severely atrophied or in some cases the tissues had simply disappeared. So was the soft tissue injury that the surgeons saw in Pat's hip images actually damage from her cobalt hip? In addition, the femur wasn't getting its blood supply. Working with a small team and a modest grant, he was able to determine that the problem was not in the surgical procedure, but in the hip implant itself. Some patients had these "invisible pathologies" even though they had no complaints. In addition to soft tissue damage, this UK orthopedic surgeon found in one of his patients that metal debris had gotten behind the cup and penetrated the pelvic bone almost to the gall bladder. Some cases required pelvic reconstruction using bone grafting. None of these problems showed up in imaging. Invisible pathology indeed. Consider this the next time you get any kind of imaging done.

What a mess and now what to do for Pat? This was a huge problem. She just had a hip revision and it would be difficult to justify another revision for a few reasons. First, we would have to find an orthopedic surgeon who believed that metal-on-metal cobalt hip implants could cause a neurological issue. Even if we did, the surgeon would have to know how to properly perform the surgery. It required more that just swapping out one implant for another. If any toxic material had penetrated bone, that would have to be removed as well. There still was no guarantee that even if the revision was done properly it would resolve Pat's cognitive issues. Results varied from patient to patient. Some made dramatic recoveries and some were less successful. Then there was the question of whether the Canadian single payer medical system would approve of another hip revision after her recent surgery. After years of the medical system's failure to resolve Pat's medical issues, the horrible experience of being sent home with a broken hip joint, being abused by giving her an antipsychotic just because she needed to go the bathroom, Pat was not only burned out but was now afraid of any kind of clinical environment. We were at an impasse and now we were going to have to live with this curse.

As if the hip implant wasn't enough, I happened to be watching the news on television when a commercial appeared for class action suits for gadolinium poisoning. This piqued my interest. I got the results for the heavy metal urinalysis that Pat had done in 2015. The panel for the heavy metals tested included gadolinium. At the time, I concentrated on mercury and lead because they were well-known neurotoxins. When Pat was first diagnosed with hemochromatosis, her iron levels were twenty-six times higher than normal. The heavy metal urinalysis results showed her lead eleven times higher than normal, mercury was ten times higher, but gadolinium was sixty-seven times higher than safe levels! Now here's the thing gadolinium is the contrasting agent used in MRI imaging. Gadolinium is a rare earth element and as such is rarely found in nature. So the only source for gadolinium toxicity is from its use as a contrasting agent in MRI imaging. Now if I was asked the rhetorical question, "where did she get the gadolinium from?" I had an answer: your fucking MRI. I was never one to go to see a doctor, but if someone talked about medically induced injury or death I would be the first guy to buy a tin foil hat for you. Medically induced injury was conspiracy talk to me, but not anymore. Whether medically induced injury is intentional or due to incompetence hardly matters to those who are injured. The medical/industrial complex now had a lot to answer for to me personally.

Gadolinium is known to be toxic to mitochondria, the liver, the nervous system and other cell tissues. It can accumulate in organ tissues including the brain. Now I was wondering if Hahnemann had been correct in concluding that the global distribution they saw in Pat's brain was iron. Since Pat had hemochromatosis, I thought they were right, but now I wasn't so sure. Could it have been gadolinium? Only a biopsy would be able to tell the difference. The gadolinium contrasting agents are classified as drugs and their formulation includes a chelating agent. Chelators are drugs that are capable of binding onto metals and carrying them out of the body mostly through urine and feces. The chelating agent used in gadolinium contrasting agents has been known to become chemically unbound while in storage. The unbound chelator not only fails in its function to rid the body of the gadolinium but now is a free radical roaming in the body. This can be a real problem because these chelators are not inert but are chemically active. The basic chemical used for all the contrast agents is DTPA and it has been shown that it can deplete essential nutrients including calcium. It does this by attaching to calcium's binding site, but the problem doesn't end there. Gadolinium is the most effective channel blocker for calcium that has ever been identified and since it is now being retained and not removed, it also interferes with calcium's role in the human body. The human body does use calcium, but has no biological use for gadolinium. It never ceases to amaze that mainstream medicine will use substances like heavy metals that are known to be extremely toxic. What are their justifications for taking such a risk? Some people may not suffer health problems from heavy metals for several reasons, but others can have their health permanently ruined. Some patients can have their health compromised from just one exposure to gadolinium contrasting agents. For those people, slogans like "doing the most good for the most people" or "the benefits outweigh the risks" are not a consolation. Some research suggests that up to 25 percent of gadolinium may not be excreted and some researchers have gone so far as to see retained gadolinium as a category of disease all by itself. Gadolinium deposition disease. This is not acceptable.

I want to go over one more topic before I finish this chapter. The functional medicine doctor had made a huge improvement with Pat's gastrointestinal tract, but she still would have irregular bowel movements that could cause her considerable pain and discomfort. She had some anxiety that was ongoing with intense flair ups and we needed to find a way to mitigate these issues. The drop seizures were by far the most dangerous problem. The drop seizures could happen at any time of the day, but they most often occurred in the middle of the night when needed to go to the bathroom. The drop seizures were so unpredictable and she could have several in a day for several days and then no occurrence for several weeks. The risk for these seizures went up exponentially when she was stressed and this was another reason to find a way to reduce her anxiety. We had learned by now that anti-anxiety medications were out of the question. Pain medications caused constipation and were not an option for helping with her gut pain. We needed to find a solution. Prior to Pat's hip revision, I had been looking into the uses of medical cannabis. Pat worked with Canadian military personnel going to and coming back from Afghanistan and knew that cannabis was used successfully to help combat veterans suffering with PTSD. The physiotherapist that was coming to the house said that she had one long-term patient who was using medical cannabis for pain management. She said that several other of her clients had started using it for chronic pain as well.

For a deeper dive on the benefits of medical cannabis, I first went to some of the leading hospitals to find what their opinion was on its benefits and effectiveness. There were several medical conditions that mainstream medicine was using medical cannabis to treat. Medical cannabis was being used to help patients with Alzheimer's disease, HIV/AIDS, cancer, Crohn's disease, epilepsy and seizures, glaucoma, multiple sclerosis, severe or chronic pain and severe nausea. Mainstream medicine has mixed results, but cannabis continues to be used in treatment and researched. Research in the effectiveness of medical cannabis has been hampered by the US Drug Enforcement Administration (DEA), which classes marijuana as a schedule I drug along with heroin and hallucinogenics. This discourages research dollars for funding medical cannabis studies.

As I started to research on medical cannabis, it didn't take long before I was introduced to a new term: the endocannabinoid system. The human body already has a built-in binding site for cannabis. It exists because the human body produces it's own cannabinoids. The endocannabinoid system was a by product discovery researching the effects of THC (the psychoactive component of cannabis). Ironically, the discovery was the result of studies commissioned to prove the dangers of marijuana. Similarly, endorphins, the body's own morphine, was discovered when researching the effects of the narcotic opium. The first naturally occurring cannabinoid that the human body produces was anandamide and since then several other natural cannabinoids have been revealed. There are receptor sites for the endocannabinoid system throughout the body and they affect several bodily systems. It seems, in whatever capacity it serves, it acts primarily as a modulator. It helps with pain relief, regulates mood and emotions and may reduce anxiety and depression. This modulating quality can act as an immunosuppressor and this why people with immunodeficiency diseases have positive results. I found the country of Israel has done more research in medical cannabis than anywhere else and has integrated its use in their mainstream medical system to treat several health issues. Science has only scratched the surface in understanding the body's endocannabinoid system.

I spent fifteen months looking into the effectiveness of medical cannabis. The available research convinced me that using medical cannabis was worth a try. I always took into consideration anecdotal evidence/experiences in making decisions and the tipping point to give this a try came from a family member who was battling chemo sickness from his cancer treatments. The $1500/month drug to fight chemo sickness worked a bit, but not always. A friend suggested to try cannabis. He said that one or two puffs off a joint and the chemo sickness vanished. Since he was also a doctor, his experience added credibility. Since Pat's health problems in large measure were caused by toxicities I didn't want to just buy street pot not knowing anything about how it was grown or where. We looked at licensed medical cannabis producers' websites and found that each batch was tested by an independent laboratory for heavy metals, pesticides, mould and other toxins. We started with a 50/50 combination of THC and CBD, but eventually found that THC by itself was the most effective. We could also self-dose as needed. If Pat was going through rough patches we could increase the dose or not use it at all when she was doing well. Pat was not going to smoke it, so we used oils in smoothies. It seemed to be help with pain and anxiety, but most importantly it was very effective in mitigating the drop seizures. If drop seizures were coming on, she would take it immediately and, within thirty minutes at the most, the drop seizures were brought under control. Once again our medical metric was results and this was achieved. Outside of supplements to help with her gut, this is the only drug that she now uses.

TOO LITTLE, TOO LATE

Maybe the trick
is to just breathe....
so I've been told.
The rhythm of in and then out
is one of the essences that we
experience in this life.
It's good to return to an essence
once in a while...
don't you think?
Just....breathe

At beginning of this book, I said that I procrastinated in writing an account of our experience because the journey wasn't complete. Medicine and health issues are much like Leonardo da Vinci's famous quote, "art is never finished, only abandoned". Ideally, medicine would clearly define a health issue and apply a solution that fits the problem. Human biology is usually far too complicated for such a simplistic view. Many times medical problems can have more than one underlying source. The reaction to these underlying issues can also vary from patient to patient. There is no one size fits all. Environmental contributors to health problems can also vary from region to region. Then there is aging. Aging will wear out the human body regardless of health problems. We are not immortal and no one gets out of this life without dying. So medicine and health is very much like da Vinci's adage and much of human health and disease ends up being a management task. After fourteen years of deteriorating health, thousands of hours of doing our own investigating and investigations done at some of the best hospitals in the world, we were returning full circle to the beginning and we know enough now to come to some educated conclusions. We also have come to the heart-breaking conclusion that Pat's health will never be restored and the frustrating conclusion that her health problems may have been resolved if she had been properly treated earlier.

Fourteen years is a long time. So where are we at now after all the investigations and revelations? Well, for one, I'm exhausted. Pat isn't interested in any more investigations and has become very disillusioned with medicine. She is mistrustful and afraid of any clinical setting. She will continue the recommended supplements for her gut and the use of medical cannabis for pain and managing anxiety, but she is not interested in any more investigations. This disappoints me, but I don't blame her. Pat, a once strong, intelligent and beautiful woman, is broken in health and in spirit. This medical odyssey started with a cynical diagnosis of Alzheimer's disease to oust her from her medical practice. We wasted five years of precious time with mainstream medicine that produced no results. Five years lost that could have made the difference to a full recovery. I am convinced, if a full recovery was not possible, she would likely not have gotten as sick as she is now. Only through hindsight do we realize that Pat's health problems were either iatrogenically induced (iatrogenic: injury caused by a doctor or medical system) or underlying contributors that mainstream medicine not only dismisses out of hand but ridicules. Any of mainstream medicine's investigations would be best described as intellectual indulgences that may contribute to the greater body of scientific knowledge, but are clinically useless. Mainstream medicine has no idea how to treat neurological disorders and their pharmacological treatments can be physically addictive and have side effects worse than the existing symptoms.

Our journey revealed that Pat's health issues had more than one underlying cause; this wasn't a surprise to me. What came as a surprise was the treatments from the alternative/complementary approaches that led to improvement were first discovered by mainstream medicine, but had been abandoned. A case in point is leaky gut syndrome. Mainstream medicine all but ignores leaky gut and many doctors ridicule the diagnosis despite leaky gut syndrome having hundreds of peer-reviewed studies confirming it. I was encouraged when I read testimonials from online leaky gut groups where people with speech/memory issues like Pat had their problems resolved after the balance in their gut had been restored. It doesn't seem logical that gut dysfunction could affect brain function, but there is a connection between the gut and the brain known as the gut/brain axis. These two organs are connected both physically and chemically. Neuron cells are usually associated to brain anatomy, but the gut has five times the number of neurons than found in the brain. The gut also produces some of the neurotransmitters that the brain uses. Some of the gut's microbes are part of the building blocks forming the all-important blood/brain barrier that protects the brain. This is also a good example that medical conditions need to be treated holistically rather that attempting to treat the body as a collection of component parts.

Another case in point is heavy metal toxicity. I have grown very weary and impatient when I hear the rhetorical question "where did Pat get the heavy metals from?" A little research reveals that there are several sources for heavy metal exposure. The science and medical community knows that heavy metal toxicity can cause many health issues including neurological problems. The standard practice for medical investigations is to rule out potential issues in an attempt to arrive at a definitive diagnosis as much as possible. Since there are many sources for heavy metal exposure, heavy metal testing should be included in the standard battery of tests. One reason that it is not tested for is because the medical community only considers acute exposure like in an industrial accident and ignores continuous low-level exposure that builds over time. At the same time, the medical community knows that the damage from iron overload due to hemochromatosis happens from the build up of iron over time. The medical system needs to stop cherry picking the science it chooses to believe.

I devoted years to finding a solution for Pat's health issues and now that mission was over. However, habits do not change over night. Have you ever had an experience when something happens or something is said that remains in the back of your mind that doesn't feel right and keeps nagging you? The orthopedic surgeon who did Pat's original hip replacement in 2006 said something that I never forgot. He said that Pat's hip had been deteriorating over many years. He suggested, for example, it may have been triggered from a sports injury going as far back as her high school. This speculation was a curiosity for me at the time that I never followed up on. Pat was never into sports other than swimming, which is low impact. So, if her hip had been deteriorating over many years, what could have caused it? The official diagnosis was osteoarthritis of the hip. Nobody in her family suffered from arthritis in any form that I knew of. My approach to understanding medical issues was reviewing the available science from mainstream and complementary medicine in combination with anecdotal experiences of patients and their families. One resource that I virtually ignore all to often is my own intuitive sense. At the time, the liver damage was a great concern and the issue of joint damage fell off my radar screen. Even after learning along the way that hemochromatosis could cause joint damage, I didn't connect the dots. Could Pat's hip degeneration have been caused by her hemochromatosis?

The consensus of the medical community is that osteoarthritis due to hemochromatosis only occurs in the smaller finger joints. Hip joint damage from hemochromatosis would be considered rare. By now, I am well acquainted with talking point medicine and claims of rarity or exceptions to the rule. I know now that these cliches can put patients at risk and I believe they are designed to drive medicine in directions that serve the medical industry more than what is in the best interest for the patient. Cliche medicine excludes testing for rare cases, resulting in those patients falling through the cracks, leaving them untreated. Talking point diagnoses can be the kiss of death in certain circumstances and this kind of faux medicine needs to be confronted. Could Pat's damaged hip have been caused by hemochromatosis? The answer to this interesting forensic medical question wouldn't help Pat at this point, but I thought I would look into it anyway.

Osteoarthritis to the hip joint may be rare, but the disease is not. It is estimated that one in 300 people of northern European descent have hemochromatosis. That is a high ratio. It highest with people who are of Celtic descent. Pat was Scottish on both sides of her family. If you're Irish, you have a one in four chance of having the genes for hemochromatosis. Most of the doctors I spoke to had heard about hemochromatosis in medical school and received a couple of lectures on the subject, but that's it. In Atlantic Canada with its high concentration of people who are of Celtic descent, I was hard pressed to find anybody who had heard of it. In addition, there is a large population of people in the region who are of French Acadian descent and Acadians are genetically Celts as well. So how can this most common genetic disorder be unknown in this high-risk population? More importantly, why isn't there general testing to find who has the disease? Wouldn't this be a good preventative measure considering how iron overload can ravage the body? Without knowing the actual number of people who have the disease, then how can there be any claims that osteoarthritis of the hip is rare? Such a claim is baseless and is just a guess. How many people have died from liver cancer due to undiagnosed hemochromatosis? Iron overload is not restricted to damaging livers. It can damage other organs including the brain. Diseases arising from hemochromatosis are all preventable because once the disease is diagnosed it is very manageable.

One of the leading authorities for hemochromatosis lives in Canada and Pat had spoken to him a few times on the phone when she first found out she had the disease in 2007. He offered to see Pat even though he wasn't doing clinical work. She didn't take him up on the offer at the time because she was still in practice and couldn't schedule time in to travel to Ontario. I had watched several of his lectures online years ago and I thought I would refresh my memory by watching them again. My perspective on medicine had changed and I thought listening again to the lectures I might gain a better understanding about the subject. In one of his lectures he didn't think widespread screening for HH in the general public was warranted. He referenced a decades-long Danish heart study. Hemochromatosis researchers were given access to the blood samples and found that many study participants had tested positive for hereditary hemochromatosis. The research subjects did not know they had the genetic mutation for HH and hadn't developed any health complications attributed to the disease. Based on this finding, the conclusion was that widespread testing for hemochromatosis was unwarranted. However, considering the potential damage that can result from this disease, is it really a wise public health policy not to conduct widespread testing at least for the higher risk groups? If Pat had been tested for hemochromatosis and monitored for iron overload, she would have avoided the debilitating complications from this disease that ruined her health and life.

Doing the most good for the most people, the benefits outweigh the risks and preventative medicine are all cliche talking points that the medical community regularly repeats. I think screening for HH in the general public is warranted and I'll use these metrics too for my rationalizations.

Doing the most good for the most people

I think that a compassionate society would all be able to agree that a medical system should be able to take care of the most vulnerable patients among us. Patients who face life-threatening illness or treating patients as early as possible before it is too late is what most people would expect from a just medical system. I've postulated earlier in this book that patients who do not fall into the "most people" category are probably the most vulnerable patients. Undiagnosed HH illustrates my point of view very well. The HH statistics gleaned from the Danish cardiac study suggested that widespread testing was not warranted because a large number of the study subjects who had HH did not develop iron over load and suffer the damage that could arise from it. However, there are people with HH who do develop serious life-threatening diseases like cancer and, as in Pat's case, cirrhosis of the liver. These patients do not fall into the most people category and the price for that distinction can cost them their lives. There are many patients suffering from other illness besides HH who get thrown under the bus because they too do not fall into the "most people" category. A medical system that was patient-oriented instead of system-oriented would go a long way to solving this problem. There are doctors who are reformers in several different fields of medicine who advocate for this very approach.

The benefits outweigh the risks

This is an easy one. There is no risk for the patient for early screening of HH. The Danish study referenced above stated that the research subjects did not know they had HH and hadn't developed any health complications attributed to the disease. How does this logic reconcile for when Pat was in practice there was general screening in the population for colon cancer from ages fifty and up even for people who had no family history and showed no signs or symptoms of the disease. The screening for health issues and diseases by mainstream medicine is based on statistics. Statistics may provide an air of legitimacy, but there's a problem. Statistics compiled for diseases like liver disease or osteoarthritis without taking into account that they arose from HH is not providing a complete picture. The cost for hemochromatosis genetic testing is cheaper than testing for other genetic diseases and is even less expensive than a blood ferritin test. Widespread genetic testing for HH is far less expensive than treating the diseases that may arise from it. To put it another way, the benefits from genetic HH testing would far outweigh the cost of not doing so. This does not include the human cost for those who have gotten seriously ill or died from diseases arising from HH.

Preventative medicine

It's difficult for me to take seriously any claims that the medical system is dedicated to the idea of preventative care when its conclusion that widespread screening for HH is unwarranted. If mainstream medicine were consistent with its screening policies maybe this could be overlooked, but their policies are varied. The conclusion against genetic testing when framed within the parameters of doing the most good for the most people, preventative medicine or the benefits outweigh the risk is wrong. Genetic testing for HH would be a sound public health policy that would serve everyone's best interests.

Not only do patients slip through the cracks, but also doctors who do go the extra mile digging deeper for their understanding of medicine for the benefit of their patients. An astute rheumatologist from McGill University Health Centre stumbled onto the connection between HH and osteoarthritis from one of the patients under his care. His patient was complaining about ankle pain and insisted that it was due to being HH positive. He had his doubts because his rheumatology textbooks stated that osteoarthritis due to HH usually involved the second and third knuckles in the hand. He was able to isolate the pain was coming from the patient's "hind foot" and not the ankle. He like most rheumatologists only connected osteoarthritis and hemochromatosis to patients who were already known to be HH positive. Despite his doubts, he started investigations with his other osteoarthritic patients when presented with pain coming from the "hind foot". He started paying attention to his patients who were complaining of ankle/hind foot pain. He started testing these patients for HH when complaining of this symptom and found many tested positive even though no other symptoms were present. A 2014 American College of Rheumatology meeting confirmed the hind foot problem was an early indicator of hemochromatosis long before the more common symptoms for HH. How is it that this early indication for HH is not common knowledge within the medical community? Early detection for any disease can dramatically increase the chance for a successful outcome in treating it. Mainstream medicine is completely dropping the ball in this case, particularly since hemochromatosis is so common.

The silliest excuse I heard against genetic testing came from one of the acclaimed Canadian hemochromatosis researchers. He said if patients knew they were HH-positive, they would be running to the doctor for every little symptom worrying that it might be a HH symptom. Parents of HH positive children would be a particularly anxious group. He reasoned that, since most HH carriers do not go on to develop any serious illness, then why cause alarm to the general public? He said that his career included clinical experience. Maybe so, but this assumption didn't come from the clinical work done in a busy family practice. Pat would say that on any given day 25% of the people she saw in the office didn't need to be there. The worried well and anxious parents are already part of the patient population. This hemochromatosis expert and public health officials essentially hiding hemochromatosis from the public is an example of elitist, top-down medicine. The current climate of cancel culture has created an "expert" class that can't be questioned, shielding them from scrutiny.

How many people are walking around HH positive and don't know it? How many parents have HH-positive children and don't know it? How do you think these parents would feel if one of their HH-positive kids went on to develop a deadly disease only to find out afterward that it could have been avoided? Policymakers are stepping out of the bounds of their mandate when they keep the public in the dark about this genetic disease. It is the duty of public health officials to inform the public and give individuals the opportunity to decide for themselves whether they want to get tested or not. This is the height of arrogance. If hemochromatosis were an incurable death sentence, a rational argument could be made to not alarm the general public. This not the case with HH because it can be successfully managed and people can live their lives normally.

So was Pat's osteoarthritis of the hip caused by hemochromatosis? This is an important question. If hemochromatosis did cause her hip degeneration, then it could have been avoided if she had known she was HH positive. The simple maintenance program would have controlled iron overload and saved her hip from deteriorating. Saving her hip means she wouldn't have needed a hip replaced with a poisonous metal-on-metal chromium/cobalt prosthetic. Neither would she had developed liver disease. General testing for HH in Atlantic Canada with its high population of people of Celtic descent, a known risk group, could dramatically avoid suffering for many people. This is a catastrophic failure by the medical system and public health regulatory agencies whose mandate is to protect patients.

The final conclusion is that two of Pat's biggest health issues were caused by the medical system itself. The failure of the medical system to screen for hemochromatosis resulted in osteoarthritis of her hip, leading to an avoidable hip replacement that caused cobalt poisoning. The other was gadolinium toxicity from the contrasting agent that is used in MRIs. There were contributors to Pat's health issues that mainstream medicine dismisses. Not only was the contribution of heavy metals, for example, ignored, symptoms were wrongly diagnosed and wrong treatments were applied and the side effects caused Pat to get sicker. I know I am laying myself wide open for criticism because I have no medical training, but the ineptitude of the medical establishment gave me licence to come to my own conclusions. Be that as it may, the bottom line is that mainstream medicine produced no results. My perception of medicine has been completely upended. Too much of mainstream medicine is a facade and is a coalition of business interests and regulatory agencies populated by people who are there to line their pockets and feed their egos with the power they wield. This needs to be laid bare for all to see and reform of the system is critical for public safety. We learned a lot and at the same time have nothing to show for it. Maybe our story will help others avoid pitfalls in their health care and if this book helps one patient and their family avoid the trouble that we had, then this book will not have been written in vain.

CONCLUSIONS

When the dust settles, hopefully something honest is left behind

"Be not afraid", Matthew 17:7. This phrase is found throughout the Old and New Testaments. Good advice. What I found in my sixty-plus years in life is that people believe what they want to believe. This goes for patients and for doctors. In the spirit of "pay it forward" I would share what we learned on this medical odyssey and received mixed results. I would have thought, since Pat was a physician for twenty-five years, that what we learned would give people pause to consider our conclusions. Some people did, but others met our opinions with skepticism and several times anger. Many patients did not want to consider what we learned because it didn't jibe with what they wanted to believe. Some of their objections were that the medical system couldn't be that corrupt or inept. Some particularly here in Canada were offended of our criticisms of the government medical monopoly because it was a source of national pride for them. I found that most Canadians who were offended were never sick themselves and hadn't any experience of what it's like to be a patient in the system. It took me a while to realize our critique of the system caused some to be afraid. They couldn't face any doubts that the medical system would fail them in their hour of need. I understand that, but being afraid to confront the shortcomings of the health system and not getting involved in your personal health issues could cost you your life. A Canadian health watchdog group estimates that 28,000 Canadians a year die from iatrogenically induced death. Some groups in the US place iatrogenic death as the second or third leading cause of death. Health issues can be overwhelming to understand, but not insurmountable. It is doable, so don't be afraid to get involved in your own health care. Patience and persistence will get you through. Doctors are not trained in reading technical papers either, so you are on even ground with them.

To my surprise, skepticism was even greater with many doctors, but when I thought it over I shouldn't have come as a surprise at all. I naively thought that doctors would be interested in what we learned and how it might benefit the patients under their care. All along our journey, I cross referenced what we found in alternative medicine with mainstream medicine for our due diligence in making decisions. Primary care physicians are the natural contact point for getting information on mainstream medicine's point of view. Since we had been moving around for several years, Pat had several primary care physicians and we experienced a range of responses in our encounters with them. I would have thought that a doctor would appreciate a patient who knew doctor "speak". Not so. After all, doctors also need information and in Pat they had a patient/doctor who could provide more detailed information than their average patient. Only one of Pat's doctors appreciated the fact that she was a doctor. This doctor even acknowledged that I most likely knew more about Pat's health issues than he did. He listened to our experiences, but our appreciation for his candour and openness became short-lived. The results of the liver imaging he ordered were shoddy work and completely contradicted the two reports done at a private MRI clinic and the ultrasound from Hahnemann hospital. I knew what happened. I understand the need to work cooperatively with colleagues in one's work environment, but he abandoned his responsibility as an advocate for Pat just for the sake of getting along with "his" radiologist.

Pat's other PCPs did not extend professional respect to her and were not open to what we had learned about the treatments that benefited her. Pat wasn't expecting special treatment for being a physician nor did she want to micro manage her care, but that didn't mean she was going to be passively silent. This was going against the grain for many doctors' clinical experience. Many patients are passive in their medical care and do whatever their doctor tells them to. On the other hand there are doctors who want their patients to be passive, making their job easier. I am not a mind reader, but to accurately understand any human interaction requires insight into reading people. I had the advantage of having spent a lot of time with doctors over the years and saw how hospital politics can work. There can be several reasons why doctors prefer passive patients, but I have grown to be impatient with arrogant doctors who haven't time for their patients. If a doctor wants to indulge their egos, I'm a willing sparring partner for you. If the guiding principle of medicine is "first do no harm", then a prerequisite characteristic for being a doctor must be humility. There is no place for arrogance in medicine. Medicine and the sciences require self questioning and brutal honesty for truth and accuracy to be revealed.

Doctors are perfectly content taking care of their patients. After all, that's why they got into medicine. They have little time or interest in the bureaucracy of medicine. Patients are perfectly content with a hands-off attitude, leaving their health care to their doctors. Unfortunately, this has created a vacuum that has allowed an unholy alliance between the medical industry and medical professionals who have created an elite, top-down medical paradigm. Bureaucracy doctors are much like the corporate ladder climbers found in any industry and they enjoy the power of position that they wield. The result is both sides of the equation of the medical/industrial complex prioritizes its interests ahead of the patients it serves. Protocols like standards of care have also constrained physicians, sometimes against their own better judgment in treating their patients. Some doctors have left medicine altogether because they couldn't reconcile their ethical standards and remain in the system. Other doctors add complementary medical approaches to try to work around the constraints in the system. There have been significant advances in certain areas of medicine, but, when the current paradigm of care essentially creates a wedge between doctor and patient, I'm not so sure if it can be said that medicine has been improved overall. There are doctors advocating for reform, but they are challenging entrenched orthodoxy. One Canadian emergency room doctor has put forth reforms that are patient-centred instead of process-centred. He argues that his proposed reforms would reduce wait times for patients. Reduced wait times would mean more patients seen, increasing hospital revenue. He also argues that the efficiency of the emergency departments would reduce operating costs. Time is money even in monopoly single-payer government medical systems. When frontline doctors are ignored, then the medical system has truly lost sight of the forest for the trees. Although mainstream medicine cannot be discredited out of hand, it still can be said that there is enough dysfunction that serious reform is needed.

Message for doctors

Maybe a half-dozen times a year, Pat would attend an information session hosted by pharmaceutical companies touting "scientific" papers on their products. The session was preceded by a dinner and cocktails and spouses were invited as well. I ate so much lobster at these dinners that I couldn't care less if I ever have this delicacy again. There is a popular conception that doctors get kickbacks for the drugs they prescribe and are given gifts like free trips. I have no idea if this is common or even true. It was never offered to Pat, but she wouldn't have accepted it anyway. Mind you, the marketing departments of companies train their sales reps in client profiling and have a pretty good idea on how to approach individual doctors. Regardless of any perks offered to doctors, a book written by a

Canadian doctor detailing the influence of the medical industry on physicians revealed doctors are mostly influenced by the pens and prescription pads displaying the company logo them. Doctors use these items hundreds of times every day and that passive exposure influences the doctor enough to favour the company's products. It's that easy to sway the human mind.

When Pat first started her medical practice, the physician community was like a close-knit family. There was a lot of cooperation among them and she was able to call a specialist to consult about one of her patients any time, even if that specialist had a day off and was not on call. By the time she ended her practice, the physician community had increased twenty-fold and the physician family environment was long gone. Now if you called an off-duty doctor for a consult you needed to be prepared to get your head bitten off. Tempers had become short and doctors were suffering from burnout. The culture at the hospital over the years had become very toxic.

Generally, there are doctors who do their job seeing and treating their patients. Then there are the political doctors. These doctors are busy with committees, policymaking and basically creating their own little empires. The hospital where Pat had her privileges had the most draconian, top-down administration of any hospital in the province. This brand of toxic work-place bullying can be found to varying degrees at many hospitals. One doctor in Quebec found himself in the crosshairs of his own professional college. He was persecuted purely for political reasons and it had nothing to do with his medical professionalism. It was eventually settled out of court, but he believed he was targeted because he had a clinic that operated outside the single-payer government-run medical system. There are strong advocates for the Canadian single-payer medical systems that detest private clinics. When he was called before a tribunal, he was missing a piece of information they requested and he told them he wasn't sure if he could provide it. The response from the tribunal was not to worry because they had more investigative resources than Canada's premier law enforcement agency, the Royal Canadian Mounted Police! The lawyer representing him also represented other doctors that were facing similar problems with physician governing bodies and two of them died by suicide from unrelenting pressure. Their suicides was directly documented to the professional assassination they were going through.

Self-reflection is an acquired skill. I have done a lot of self-reflection during our journey to avoid falling into the trap of bitterness and vengeful thinking for the shameful treatment that Pat had to endure. Physicians need to question themselves more than many other professions because of the responsibility they have in caring for people's health. The physician community needs to take a good hard look at itself. The shocking epidemic of death by suicide among physicians and medical students is proof that something is very wrong. Death by suicide is a blight and a disgrace that every physician should be ashamed of. How many proud parents have sent their kids off to medical school only to later to get the tragic news that their child died by suicide? Most documented suicides of medical students had no history of attempted suicides in the past or any suicide ideation. Suicides decimates families and many times the loved ones left behind never recover. How can a medical system treat patients for depression to avoid suicide when the highest suicide rate comes from their own ranks? How can society trust a sick, dysfunctional medical school system to produce the caring, skilled physicians that it depends on for its health? The high suicide rate in the profession is an alarm bell that something is fundamentally wrong in medicine.

There has always been a toxic competitive streak in the medical community starting even in medical school. The equivalent of an entire graduating class of medical students die by suicide every year in the United States. A medical doctor took it upon herself to bring attention to the high suicide rate with physicians and published a book of suicide letters from physicians and medical students who had taken their own lives by suicide. Most of the suicides of medical students didn't result from the pressure of the workload but from the bullying from their own instructors. Astonishingly, a medical student said that the instructor in her very first class told the students that some of them would die from suicide before they graduated. He went on and told the class how to successfully kill themselves. For an instructor to counsel medical students on how to kill themselves is a disgrace and should be a chargeable offence. What kind of an asshole instructor would ever say such a thing? What ethical standard is being set for medical student, where ethics for the profession is everything?

Most of the suicide letters in the book were students who had dreamed of becoming a doctor/healer from a very young age. The healing arts is an old, honourable profession and worthy goal. My question for medical students is what kind of a healer will you be after being subjected to the abuse that seems to be so common in medical schools? How do you reconcile the abuse of medical schools if it is your goal to become a compassionate healer? Finally, if the medical school system is this dysfunctional, is it an indicator that the very system you will practise medicine in will also be this dysfunctional? These are questions that need to be considered for the profession you chose, but more importantly these questions need to be asked on behalf of your patients. These questions also need to be asked before the mountainous accumulation of student debt and assuming the responsibilities of raising families and paying mortgages, all of which could influence your decision in doing what's right. Many of the letters of medical students who graduated with a degree found themselves so psychologically injured by the experience that compassion was beat out of them and now medicine was just a job. If you're a patient, do you really want to be treated by someone who essentially is suffering from PTSD? The toxic aspects of the medical profession need to be rooted out for the sake of physicians and for the patients they treat. The negative aspects of the doctor profession have deep roots and will not be easy to turn around if indeed it's even possible. There are powerful headwinds against reforming the medical system from political and industrial interests and even from medicine's own governing bodies. The medical governing bodies have sold out doctors and patients and the axiom "first do no harm" is not their guiding principle anymore. However, it needs to start somewhere and it will take honesty, courage and full disclosure backed up by truth and not agendas for meaningful reform to occur.

Message for patients

The general consensus of the medical consuming public is that medicine is a scientific/evidence-based system. When I talk to people, it becomes clear that their perception of the "science" in medicine is the same as the sciences that they studied in high school and post-secondary schools. This is a very simplistic and inaccurate way to view the role of science in medicine. Human biology is far too complicated to try to equate it to the concepts of scientific constants like the speed of light or the gravitational constant. If medicine were as definitive as the hard sciences, then there would never be a need for a second opinion. The perception of medicine being like hard science is reinforced by high-tech medical imaging equipment like MRIs. Expensive, high-tech equipment is an impressive example of scientific applications used in medicine, but there is a serious short coming with technologies like this. We had radiologists who drew totally opposite conclusions in reading the same image! Hard sciences produce replicable results despite who is conducting the experiment. Second opinions are good medicine, but completely opposite opinions do not contribute accurate diagnoses. How does such a wide divergence of opinions occur? Do radiologists get completely different training based on which medical school they attend? Is one radiologist correct and the other radiologist incompetent? If so, how did an incompetent radiologist graduate medical school? These questions contradict the notion that medicine is like the hard sciences and should alert the medical consumer to be buyer beware. Discrepancies in medicine are common. I know a married couple who are both doctors and the husband will prescribe selective serotonin reuptake inhibitors (SSRI) to his patients diagnosed with depression. His wife will not because she thinks that SSRIs can cause neurological damage. Here's another question to ponder: how do we have an opioid crisis? Out of the 2500 patients Pat had in her practice, only two were prescribed opiates to deal with pain management. The black market is fuelling the opioid crisis, but so are prescriptions for narcotics from doctors.

Patient profiling and standards of care have replaced a very important component of medicine, the intuitive sense of doctoring that comes from experience and the endowed natural talent of a good physician. Profiling and standards of care remove the humanness of patients. It's bad medicine for a doctor to treat family or friends because an emotional attachment could easily cloud clinical judgment. Dispassionate, unemotional assessments are essential in properly diagnosing patients, but never at the expense of forgetting that the patient is also a unique individual. I fear that the humanness of medicine is being lost because the algorithmic approach of patient profiling and standards of care is changing the paradigm from patient-oriented to system-oriented medicine. I am not alone in this concern; some doctors have expressed concern as well. Indeed, activist doctors advocate that, for serious reform of the medical system to take place, patients need to be the centre of the paradigm.

There is another problem that indirectly removes patients from the equation. The current climate of political correctness and cancel culture discourages people to even question the "expert" class. Society needs honest truth seeking experts, not "experts" who are nothing but shills for political and business interests. I strongly suggest that patients get heavily involved in their medical care. Do not passively accept top-down medical care without question. Think of the doctor/patient relationship as a partnership where you at least hold 51 percent, putting you in control. The western society that we live in prides itself on the freedom of the individual to pursue their lives. Why would you completely capitulate the responsibility of your very person to another human being? On this specific point, I want to comment on the Canadian experience. Canada has a single-payer government-administered and publicly funded medical system. For full disclosure, I am not a socialist and do not support politburo medicine. By definition, a public medical system belongs to the public and yet most Canadians are passive and take for granted that it will be there when they need it. Most of us know that it's not easy to make a living and are mindful about our financial affairs. Does it make any sense that Canadians are hands off and disinterested in a medical system that costs billions of their taxpayer dollars? A fellow Canadian who is a socialist mentioned to me once that in a socialist system, in addition to a bill of rights, there needs to be a bill of responsibility. Whatever that means. Regardless, this seems to make sense; however, I've never heard anybody let alone a socialist suggest such a policy. I know that these sentiments put me well into controversy territory, but what needs to be acknowledged in the public versus private health care debate is that both are susceptible to cronyism.

FINAL THOUGHTS

Indeed what a strange trip it has been...I will land when I realize
my wings fell away a long time ago

On a personal note

Spirituality has always been a private matter to me. I had an internal debate whether I should bring this up and honestly I am coming out of my comfort zone talking about it. However, my faith has been so integral in getting me through this journey that I feel compelled to share the role it has played. I was raised in the Catholic Church and I've had a lifelong interest in spirituality. I continued attending Mass on and off through the years and have attended other Christian church services. I studied world religions at the college level, practised some meditative techniques and did a lot of reading on my own all in attempt at a deeper understanding of self and spirituality. Pat has played a huge part on my path to trying to be a better person. She challenged me and wouldn't let me get away with some of the crap I would try to pull from time to time. Unravelling Pat's health issues was a monumental task. I had no medical background and the learning curve was steep. Arriving at an accurate diagnosis was difficult; deciding the best treatment plan and finding a doctor who could implement it was not easy. There were so many moving parts to deal with. It is really important to be well grounded or emotions will get away from you. It is essential to have the support of people that you can trust. This was a very important missing link and I had no choice but to turn to my spirituality to fill that void. This isolation would turn out to be a blessing because I started having experiences in reading the Bible that I had never had before. Details in biblical passages seemed to appear that weren't there before. There were several "eureka" moments where passages that I knew well took on new meaning or I would gain a deeper understanding. Completely new perspectives popped out fully formed entirely outside the constructs of my own thinking or my efforts in studying the Bible. This was an interesting turn of events and an experience I had never had in my spiritual journey. I wanted to know if what I was experiencing wasn't the workings of my mind at some subliminal level because it sure seemed that some entity outside of myself was at play. Even more intriguingly, bad habits that I couldn't shake for years were stopping abruptly through no effort of my own. Not only did I not put any effort into it; I wasn't praying for them to end. I just thought of them as vices that I would just have to learn live with or work my way around them.

These experiences were disconcerting in a way. My spirituality was always initiated by me searching for answers. This was different. The best example I can think of are "invasive" thoughts, which is weird because I associate invasive thoughts as being negative. I've had "eureka" moments that resulted from hard studying or spending a lot of time on task. The eureka moments that I was experiencing from reading the Bible came rushing into my mind and had nothing to do with hard studying or deep thinking. The bad habits that ended abruptly without any impetus to explain it were like an intervention had just occurred. Any other time, unexplained phenomena like this would spook me, but these "interventions" were liberating as if a weight had been taken off my shoulders. Phrases like by the grace of God or a gift from God or even the word faith were now taking on a whole new meaning. I had read the Bible for years and gained a lot from doing so, but these experiences were a dramatic example of the Holy Spirit springing into action that left no doubt in my mind that a power outside my imagining things was making Its presence known. This was humbling, awe inspiring and I will be forever grateful for God's grace blessing me in this way. I would not have made it without these revelatory experiences and the ever-present prodding of the Holy Spirit. My prayer now is listening mostly instead of me doing all the talking. Amen.

Food for thought

There are various groups advocating for medical freedom across a broad spectrum of health issues. The groups range from conspiracy thinkers to legislative bodies introducing bills in the aim of supporting medical freedom. The driving force is a dissatisfaction with the medical status quo. The freedom over your own person is fundamental and shouldn't be taken lightly. I live in Canada, where there is a single-payer publicly funded medical system. The US has a large private insurance medical industry alongside government programs like Medicare and Medicaid. Regardless of public versus private health systems, a small group of people hold the power to make decisions on behalf of millions of people and shape the direction of the medical system. There is old cliche expression "give them an inch and they will take a mile". Algorithmic medicine like patient profiling and standards of care was already taking patients out of the equation, eroding their medical freedom. Many of us get to be pretty astute shoppers by experience, but all too many of us abandon educating ourselves as medical consumers. Are you comfortable with someone making medical decisions for you? We learned the hard way that this was a big mistake.

Pat said once that there was an unwritten rule at the hospital that if a doctor fails to elicit a DNR (do not resuscitate) order they are failing in their job. Pat hated this. She would try to inform the patient as best as she could about their medical status and let them decide for themselves if they wanted to sign off on a DNR. Why the coercion? It's not a doctor's or the medical system's business to "coerce" a patient to sign off on a DNR no matter how overwhelming the odds are for their survival. Doctors cannot say for certainty which patient could beat the odds. Doctors do not have superior moral or ethical judgment to influence a patient's decision on whether they should submit to a DNR. Coercing patients is getting dangerously close to taking away the patient's right to their own medical decisions. Physicians are in a position to exert a lot of influence. A case in point is euthanasia. There are many people who will be greatly influenced on their decision on euthanasia by a doctor's opinion. This is a tragedy because sometimes people do pull through or there could be treatments that may make a difference not available in mainstream medicine that the patient is not aware of.

I remember an instructor for a marketing class I took saying something I'll never forget: "People are motivated either by fear or greed". I hated hearing that and would prefer to think humanity is driven by higher ideals than fight or flight responses like fear and greed. Conversely, perfection is a pie-in-the-sky ideal that is beyond the reach of mere humans. However, an impetus is needed to start the pendulum swinging back in the right direction for serious reform of the medical system to take place. I think it will take the participation of doctors and patients for meaningful change to take place. There was a time when people had a sense of duty and were willing to pay the price of self sacrifice to fulfill that sense of duty. JFK famously said, "Ask not what your country can do for you, but ask what you can do for your country." We as a society have lost a lot of this attitude and it needs to be re-established. Duty and self sacrifice are virtues that cannot be quantified and it's for each of us to take up this cause within ourselves.

9 781800 465152